BEAST OF BURDEN

KYLE RICHARDVILLE

ISBN 979-8-88751-579-3 (paperback)
ISBN 979-8-88751-580-9 (digital)

Christian Faith Publishing
832 Park Avenue
Meadville, PA 16335
www.christianfaithpublishing.com

Printed in the United States of America

CHAPTER 1

Esoteric Garbage

"With liberty and happiness for all," the class half-heartedly mumbled.

"Thank you. You may all be seated," Principal Coleman said over the loudspeakers. "As you all know, this is the last day of school before summer break. Seniors, please make sure all graduation papers are in order before commencement on Saturday night. We want to say thank you to our wonderful senior class for all your hard work, and we wish you all the best in each and every one of your individual pursuits of happiness. Freshmen, sophomores, and juniors—enjoy the summer, be safe, and be ready for another great year at Morrison High in August!"

Principal Coleman ended, as she always does, by reciting the school motto, "Fly high, Eagles!"

Once Principal Coleman was finished with her daily announcements, Mrs. Simpson spoke up to her students, "Okay, okay, quiet down, class! I know it's the last day, and everybody wants to leave, but we still have today to learn. But before we get to the last lesson, I wanted to say thank you for such an amazing year. I had more fun teaching this junior class than any of the seventeen classes I've taught before you! All the students, except for a couple troublemakers, really bought into the system and gave it their all this year. I can't even begin to explain how proud I am. Teaching philosophy to students like you is the reason why I love my job! As you move into your

1

senior year and eventually on to college, just remember that all of you are special, all of you are capable of success, and all of you deserve to achieve that success." Mrs. Simpson's voice quivered, and tears filled her eyes toward the end of her speech. She cared very deeply about the well-being of each and every one of her students.

She cleared her throat, regained her composure, and continued, "All right, as you know, having already taken the final exam, today's lesson will not be tested on. However, we, on the faculty, feel that this lesson is important for the class to learn, nonetheless. Today we will be briefly introducing the wonderful concept of happiness, which you all will explore more deeply during your senior year philosophy course."

Mrs. Simpson picked up a marker and wrote HAPPINESS in big red letters on the whiteboard. "Now we all understand what happiness is. We have in each of us a sense of what makes us happy, right? Of course, we do! Puppies makes us happy. Being handed that paycheck after a long week at work makes us happy! Even chowing down on our favorite meal makes us happy! On the flip side, we also know what doesn't make us happy. Breakups make us unhappy. Pain and deaths of loved ones make us unhappy. Have you ever once stopped to think why that is?" She paused to give the class a moment to think.

She began again, "One of you may say, 'That doesn't explain why, say, watching a basketball game makes Person A happy, while at the same time making Person B unhappy and bored.' That is a very good question! Well, many of the best thinkers of modern times have thought this predicament through. Happiness, they concluded, is determined at the individual level. They go on to reason that happiness is so important that it is the fundamental aim of life that we all strive for and, taken one step further, it should be the fundamental aim of a healthy life!" Her gentle eyes and inviting smile added to the sincerity in her voice. "Think about it for a second. Has anyone in this room right now ever done something on purpose because they thought it would make them unhappy? Of course not!" she said before allowing anyone in the class to respond.

"Now I know that this is a lot of information in a very short amount of time, and I know that I don't have much more time to dig deeper into the topic, but I just want to discuss one more thing before uncaging you animals for the summer. Now we all know that the United States of America was founded out of rebellion. But what were they *really* rebelling against? High taxes on tea and stamps? Partially. There was a deeper reason behind it: freedom from oppressive forces.

"The Founding Fathers had a truly revolutionary vision for this great country when they founded it. They believed that a government should not be free to run the people. Rather, the people should be free to run the government. They believed the people should have the freedom to believe what they want to believe and pursue what they want to pursue, so long as it did not disrupt anyone else's pursuits. They described what they called the 'pursuit of happiness' as an inalienable right that every citizen of this country has. Inalienable means something that cannot be taken away from you. You deserve to pursue happiness simply because you are a person. That's the only requirement!

"In fact, you did nothing to earn it, just like you did nothing to earn your right to have constant access to an adequately safe source of drinking water. We, and I say we, meaning the United States of America, believe that restricting this right to safe drinking water is wrong and punishable. The same is said for denying a person their pursuit of happiness."

She continued, "I know this is obvious to us by now, but there was a time not so long ago when this way of thinking was not accepted by our society. We are doing a much better job now at allowing our citizens the freedom to pursue happiness without oppression. It's hard to believe that kind of hatred, bigotry, and oppression existed in this great country, but it's sadly true." Mrs. Simpson's usually cheery countenance dropped with each subsequent word. "As sad as it is, this country has many insidious stains on it that we are trying very hard to correct. The first great stain that probably comes to mind is the enslavement of African peoples against their will. The United States is also to blame for many other blatant violations of human rights and pursuits of happiness of its citizens, including women's rights, minority rights, and children's rights. Thank goodness these blatant violations have since been corrected. Slowly but surely we have moved closer and closer to eradicating all violations against all groups, including those that are not as visible but are nonetheless just as heinous."

By this point, she was pacing back and forth in front of the whiteboard at the front of the class. "To help understand the concept of the pursuit of happiness, seniors are taught about the Great Commission and its impact on American and global thought. This is no small task and will take most of the year to really delve into."

A low murmur began filling the room as many students stopped paying attention to Mrs. Simpson and began packing up their backpacks. Mrs. Simpson was not the type to raise her voice toward her students, so she became silent and looked at the class with as stern a look as they had ever seen her give them. Every student, except for one, immediately sensed the weight of Mrs. Simpson's glare and faced forward with their mouths closed shut.

"Archer," she said, "please stop putting up your things and face the front. I would also like to speak to you after class. Thank you."

Archer sighed and begrudgingly did as he was told and faced the front of the room.

"Now where was I? Oh yes! Class, I am so grateful that we finally decided to make philosophy a required course for all high school students across the country. I know that the subject of philosophy is difficult, but believe me, what you will be learning next year is the most important lesson you will ever learn. How we view the world determines how we interact with the world. How we define values and morals dictates how we treat ourselves and others. Important, right?

"Now I mentioned the Great Commission, which I know all of you have already briefly learned about in your American history class. I cannot stress enough how important it is to learn that which the Great Commission outlined in terms of freedom, liberty, oppression, and happiness. The great panel of intellectuals working on the Great Commission single-handedly changed the trajectory of America and the world, for that matter, for the better, in a way that we had never witnessed before and have not since. Class, let me just say that you are in for an amazing year of philosophy once everyone returns in August as big, bad seniors!"

Smiles went across many of the students' faces.

She finished by saying, "I want to thank you all so much again for a great year, and I can't wait to see your smiling faces in the halls again come August!" Just as she finished speaking, the final school buzz of the year went off, and the door slid open. Mrs. Simpson walked toward her desk and then turned around abruptly. "I almost forgot! Archer," she said above the roar of the crowd, "before you scurry away, would you please stay behind for a few minutes so we can speak in private? Thank you very much."

Archer stopped in his tracks, let out a sigh, and took off his backpack.

The room was soon filled with only Archer and Mrs. Simpson. "Archer, I've known you for a very long time. I remember when you would come here to be with your mom after school as she finished up her work. You were so excited to learn about anything and everything! You were so enthusiastic about doing your homework and giving your best in school! We used to call you the 'little sponge,' for how easily you soaked up your lessons! What happened between then and now?" she asked.

Archer remained silent.

"You're a very smart boy with a lot of potential, and I know you didn't try your hardest in my class. You acted disinterested, and you disengaged with me and most of your peers. You're better than that, Archer!" She put a hand on his shoulder and said, "I just want to get a deeper understanding about what's going on in your life right now and try to help. Is someone in school being mean to you?"

Archer, sitting in his chair with his legs fully extended outward and his arms and legs crossed, looked at Mrs. Simpson and said, "With all due respect, Mrs. Simpson, I don't owe you or anyone else any explanation about anything. If I may, I might even say your oppression of me right now is keeping me from pursuing my happiness of leaving this classroom and this school for the summer."

Mrs. Simpson folded her arms, grinned, and shook her head back and forth. After a few seconds, she said, "You may go, Archer."

Archer got up and slung his backpack over his shoulder.

"And don't worry, I won't tell your mom about this little meeting."

"Good," he said as he walked out of the classroom.

"Yo, Arch, what was that all about?" a boy roughly the same size as Archer said to him.

"Thanks for waiting for me, Ty. It was nothing. She thinks I'm slacking in her class, and I'm 'wasting all my potential,'" he said as he made air quotes with his fingers. "You know how that stuff goes," Archer said.

Ty laughed, threw his forearm into Archer's upper arm, and said, "Man, that's the second teacher this week! I'm glad I don't get that much attention from our teachers! Perks of being the principal's son, eh?" he said as he nudged Archer.

"Yeah, what a perk," Archer said with a chuckle as he shoved Ty back. "I'm just so sick and tired of teachers always gettin' on my case. I get that school's important. Mom's been stuffing that idea into our heads, ever since we were in diapers," he said. "And what's worse," he added, as they pushed open the doors to the outside, "is that in their daily lives, adults don't even use the stupid information they're telling us is so important to learn! Remember that gameshow where the adults do trivia against the kids in high school? The high school kids always won, and the adults would be so embarrassed that they forgot all the crap they 'learned' in school.

"It's all a big waste of time, if you ask me," Archer said, in the parking lot, leaning against his car. "Joe the plumber needs to know trigonometry to fix a broken toilet as much as a squirrel needs to learn Portuguese to bury an acorn. Both of them can do their jobs perfectly fine without all the esoteric garbage being forced down their throats. You know what I mean, Ty?"

"Dude, you've got issues," Ty said laughingly.

"You know I'm right, though!" Archer exclaimed. "Try and prove me wrong. I dare you!"

Ty smiled, shook his head, and said, "You know, I would, I really would, but I've gotta get to the gym. I'm working with a client in ten minutes, and I need to change out of my school uniform. See ya later."

"Think about what I said! We're not done talking about it!"

"Whatever you say, Arch. See you tonight at Greyson's house."

Once Ty had driven away, Archer hopped in his car, plugged in his phone, cranked up the stereo, and took the long way home. "Free at last, free at last," he said with one arm out the window and one on the wheel. Archer's family lived out in the rural parts of town, and he often found himself admiring the bucolic scenes on his way home. "No teachers, no parents, no problems" was his self-proclaimed motto for these liberating drives.

After about a half hour, Archer decided his internal battery had been recharged enough to go home. He pulled into his usual parking spot in the driveway and headed inside with his backpack slung around one shoulder. Archer walked in the house and set his backpack down in its usual spot on a hook by the front door. Just as he was about to walk upstairs to his room, he heard a familiar voice say, "You're not gonna say hi to me?"

Surprised, Archer turned around and said, "Jamie?"

"That's my name. Don't wear it out, loser."

Archer laughed and said, "What are you doing home? I thought you had a gig lined up in New York City?"

Jamie, an aspiring singer and actress, moved away from their hometown to pursue her lifelong dream of becoming famous. "Archer, you don't know the first thing about show business, so allow me to let you in on a little secret we like to say in the industry: 'Ain't no business like show business, baby.' This isn't your typical nine-to-five glamourless job. Gigs come and gigs go at a moment's notice, and that's just the way it is."

Archer listened intently to his older sister's words. He always secretly admired her drive to be famous.

"And besides," she continued, "I'm only two years out of acting school. I've got plenty of time to make the connections I need for that one big break that's gonna land me on Broadway!" she said as she posed with hands on her hips and head held high, gazing toward the ceiling.

Archer rolled his eyes and said, "Well, I hate to burst your bubble, but unless the casting director of *America, the Hateful* decides to dine in at the restaurant you find yourself waitressing at, then it probably ain't happenin', baby."

Jamie's head dropped from gazing at the ceiling to look at Archer in his eyes. "You still haven't changed a bit, have you? I was just like you, you know that. A rambunctious teen with a chip on your shoulder. A rebel without a cause. Well, let me tell you something, smart guy. The real world is coming for you. It's coming fast, and it's coming hard. It wants to tackle you into a coma that you won't be able to recover from. The only way to survive that tackle is to learn how to accept it and play by the rules."

Pouring milk over his bowl of cereal, Archer asked, "Oh yeah, and what rules are we all supposed to play by? Please enlighten me."

Jamie, now sitting across from him at the kitchen table, said, "Stop playing dumb, Arch. I know you care a lot more about stuff than you want everyone else to think. You've heard the stuff Mom and Dad preached to us our whole lives. 'Get a good education.' 'Get a good paying job.' 'Work on your score.' It sounds like politician-speak, but everything they taught turns out to be true once you graduate."

Swallowing his bite of cereal, he said, "First off, I do care about things, and I do want people to know that fact. I care about basketball and I care about my car and I care about my dog. But caring about my score is something I'll never understand. And secondly, Mom and Dad don't know what they're talking about. They've been brainwashed. The American dream isn't one-size-fits-all. As much as they think it is, it's not. In fact, I'll prove it to you," he said matter-of-factly. "Today in philosophy class, we learned that happiness is up to the individual and individual alone. Explain to me how two people can have opposing views of what makes them happy and both be right."

Jamie looked at her little brother as older siblings do when they say something immature. "Ahh, Mrs. Simpson's philosophy class. I always loved that class," she said, reminiscing. "Look, I'm not gonna say what you said is wrong, but I am gonna say that you're missing the other half of the story. Just wait until Mr. Locke's senior philosophy class. That class will set you straight."

Worried that the experience trump card had ended his chances of winning the argument, Archer thought deeply about what he was going to say next. Before he could offer his rebuttal, Jamie chimed in again. "Take me, for example. I didn't take Mom and Dad's admonitions seriously either for the longest time. It took until spring semester of senior year for something in my brain to finally understand the big picture. Since then, I've been absolutely on fire to improve my score! In fact, my score is already in the 47.58th percentile. Pretty good for a twenty-four-year-old, don't you think?" she asked boastfully.

"Mm-hmm," Archer said unenthusiastically with a mouthful of cereal.

"The point is, Archer, I wouldn't be in this position if I hadn't listened to what Mom, Dad, and Mr. Locke taught me."

Archer took another bite.

"As your most experienced and mature sibling, I'm advising that you listen to them and shape up. It's what's best for you."

"Mm-hmm," Archer said once again.

Jamie grinned. "I'm just looking out for you, little bro. I love you, and I want to see you be happy. That's what it's all about, right?"

Jamie got up from her seat at the table and plopped back down on the couch to watch TV.

Archer finished his cereal and sat on the opposite end of the couch. After watching a few minutes of TV, he spoke up and said, "Do you honestly believe in that score nonsense?"

Jamie immediately shot up. "What do you mean 'do I believe in that score nonsense?'"

"I don't know. It all seems kinda made-up, doesn't it?" Archer asked.

Jamie furrowed her brow and cocked her head to the side a bit. "I don't understand what you mean," she said.

"Like what if everyone stopped doing it? Would the world end or something?" Archer asked.

Jamie looked concerned. "Archer, I know you're just a kid, but you really can't be saying things like that. The system in place was designed by the smartest scientists and philosophers of all time. Do you really think you're smarter than them?"

Archer didn't reply.

"Let me help you. You're not," she replied. "And just so you know, it's constantly being updated to make sure it keeps up with modern discoveries and advances in society. Does that sound made-up to you?"

"I guess not," Archer said, deflated.

"There you go!" Jamie replied. "If you want, I've got some books up in my room I could give you that really helped me when I was in high school," she said as she pointed upstairs. "Oh! I've got an even better idea! We could talk to Dad tonight after dinner about what he does at work all day. We can just say we're interested in how it all works!"

"Uhh…sure…I guess that could work."

"Perfect!" she said. "I could use a good refresher on how my score is calculated too. Time flies by once you're out there in the real world actually trying to move up the scoreboard! It's like you don't even notice how quickly you move through the days and the months!"

"And why is that a good thing?" Archer asked.

"Because 'tomorrow is almost here,' right?" Jamie exclaimed. "That's not just some silly slogan they made up, you know."

Archer did not comprehend.

"Soon enough," Jamie said, patting her brother on the head, "you'll learn."

"I guess we'll just have to have this talk in a few months," Archer said.

"Great idea," she said. "By that time, you'll be armed and ready with the knowledge to efficiently improve your score, and we can have a more educated discussion."

"Sounds like a plan," Archer replied.

"You know?" Jamie said, after scrolling through TV show options. "Adrian really is a lucky boy. He understood from an early age what the almighty Happiness Quotient (HQ) is all about. Jamie was speaking about their middle brother, Adrian, who, at the time, was attending a prestigious private university in the northeast of the country. "Gosh, I wish I would have started earlier like Adrian did," she said. "I get so jealous knowing that my younger brother is already in the top twenty-fifth percentile!"

"Doesn't bother me a bit," Archer replied self-righteously.

"Do you even know what your score is?" Jamie asked.

"Nope," he replied. "I haven't looked in a long time."

"You haven't?" Jamie said, shocked. "You don't check it every day like we're supposed to?" she asked.

"I mean, I do," Archer said. "I always log in and out to get my confirmation statement, but I don't ever pay attention to what my score actually is. It seems stupid to me," he said.

"But you take your surveys at least, right?" she asked.

"Most days," Archer replied. "I usually just click through it as fast as I can, though. I can't remember the last time I actually read a question," Archer replied with a small chuckle.

Jamie looked at Archer in astonishment and scooted closer to him on the couch. "Archer," she said softly, "this isn't funny. I'm starting to get really worried about you. What's going on? Are you being bullied or something?"

Archer got up and shot back, "Why does everyone keep asking me that? There's nothing wrong with me!" Archer's face became a deep red hue. "Look, I agreed to have that stupid talk with Dad tonight, okay? Just leave me alone. End of conversation." Archer grabbed his things and marched up the stairs to his bedroom and slammed his door shut in anger.

Archer dropped his backpack on the floor and flung himself on top of his unmade bed. While lying there, his mind raced through the two conversations with Mrs. Simpson and Jamie, over and over again. "What's wrong with ME?" he asked himself rhetorically. "A better question is: what's wrong with everyone else? Life is pointless, and a stupid score isn't going to change that. We're born, we live, and we die. That's it. Most people don't even know the most rich and powerful people from a hundred years ago. And they were the most successful people in the world! Once your generation is gone…POOF! You're a nobody again, just like you were before you were born."

After a few minutes of mentally proving himself right, Archer began to feel better. He lay there, staring at the ceiling with his hands interlocked underneath his head. Beginning to feel bored, he rolled over onto his stomach with his upper body dangling over the edge. Curiosity struck, and he slid down lower to see if anything was below his bed. Archer's face lit up as he caught sight of an old shoebox. This shoebox contained relics from his childhood, like his valuable basketball cards, his old journal, and his favorite photos he chose to print out. Excitedly, he sat on the floor and lifted the lid on the box. He grabbed a stack of basketball cards and began to shuffle through them until he found his autographed Eric Muncie card with a piece of game-worn jersey. Archer felt the square piece of jersey with his finger and tried to imagine what it would be like to meet his hero. "That would be the happiest day of my life," he said.

After looking through his old cards and photos, he grabbed hold of his leather-bound journal that was lying on the bottom of the disorganized pile. Prior to high school, Archer loved to write. He documented his thoughts every night before bed, thanks to the journal he was holding that his grandfather bought him for his twelfth birthday.

Archer thumbed through his old journal entries and laughed as he read about the "life-or-death" problems in the life of a preteen. "Dear journal," one entry started. "The first day of middle school is tomorrow, and I couldn't be more nervous! All the elementary schools combined into one middle school, and I can't wait to see all the new students I've never met before. I hope they like me. Wish me luck! —AC."

Archer turned the page. "Dear journal," it began. "Well, we made it through the first day, and I think I'm in love. She's the most beautiful girl in the whole entire world. We passed each other in the hallway, and I think my jaw still hurts from it hitting the floor. More details to come. —AC." Memories of that moment flooded Archer's mind. He replayed the scene in his head like a mental home video. He could see a group of girls walking toward him with one girl, in particular, catching his eye.

Archer flipped a few more pages until he reached a page that he recognized immediately. "Dear journal, Grandpa died. Today is the worst day of my life. —AC." Archer read the next page. "Dear journal, the doctors don't know what happened to him. They think he died of old age, but he was only eighty-one and skinny and healthy. Well, skinny as far as old people go. You will not be forgotten, Grandpa. I love you. —AC." An old, familiar feeling began to well up inside of him. He had not felt this feeling in a very long time; he felt alone.

Archer's grandfather, Franklin Coleman, was his most trusted confidant, his role model, and his best friend. Franklin also loved Archer very much. He could see something special in Archer, but he suspected Archer was not a confident boy. In fact, Archer called himself "stupid" and "unpopular" many times in front of Franklin. As best as he could, he took little Archer under his wing. Their favorite hobby was going fishing at the pond on Franklin's property. He also taught Archer how to hunt, manage farm animals, ride horses, and grow food in his garden. Oftentimes they would each have a bowl of ice cream together before Archer was to leave and go home. "Don't tell your mother," he would say with a smile as he gave Archer his bowl. Archer would make the motion like he was zipping his mouth shut, and they would both enjoy their dessert. Franklin loved all his grandchildren, including Archer's siblings, but Archer seemed to cling to his grandfather more than the others. Archer placed the journal back in the shoebox, pushed it underneath the bed, and lay back down, facing the ceiling.

He began to reminisce about his grandfather. A smile, accompanied by a solitary tear rolling down his cheek, crept on to his face as he thought about all the happy memories with his grandfather. He wiped his face with the sleeve of his school uniform and closed his eyes. Images of the two of them spending time together filled his imagination, like the time Grandpa stood by as he taught Archer how to milk a cow and the time he helped him unhook the first fish he ever caught. The loneliness inside of Archer immediately began to attenuate as his grandfather's love washed over his body.

Archer, so happy and relaxed, for the first time in a long time, drifted off to sleep as the shadows in his room elongated from the afternoon rays of sunshine.

CHAPTER 2

Sign Here

Archer woke up to the sound of commotion. He wiped the half-dried slobber off his face and sat up in his bed. Something didn't quite feel right to him, but he often woke up feeling a little discombobulated after an impromptu afternoon nap, so he didn't think much of it. The sun was shining brightly through his window, so he knew it was not yet time for dinner with his family. In the meantime, Archer decided to get up out of bed and change out of his school uniform. He opened his closet and, to his surprise, found that it was not filled with his clothes. It was filled with one fancy black suit, a pair of socks, and a pair of black dress shoes. He pulled out the drawers of his dressers and found them all completely empty. "What is going on?" he asked out loud. With no other clothing options, he grabbed the outfit and tried it on. "Would you look at that," Archer said, spinning to see himself from all angles in the mirror. "It fits perfectly!" At that moment, he heard a loud commotion outside that sounded like the low hum of a crowd at a mid-July Major League Baseball game.

Archer went over to the window to investigate what was happening. Outside his window was the usual large oak tree in the yard and basketball goal in the driveway. Yet the noise persisted. Archer looked at his phone to see if that was emitting the noise, but his phone was dead. Next he checked his laptop and TV, only to find that they were also off. "Am I going crazy?" he said as he pinched himself to make sure he wasn't still asleep. Sure enough, he felt the pinch.

The intensity of the noise continued to grow. "Jamie must be watching a movie in the living room with the surround sound turned on," Archer now reasoned. He opened the door to go downstairs. Archer stopped in his tracks. Instead of seeing his staircase, he saw what looked like a bustling metropolis of people and skyscrapers. Terrified, he slammed his door shut, locked it, and threw his back against the door. Archer felt like his heart was going to pound right out of his chest. His pupils were dilated, and he knew his body was in the fight-or-flight mode that he had just learned about in anatomy class. "I've got to be dreaming," he said out loud. "There's no other explanation."

Again he pinched himself and felt the pain. He walked over to the window, and once again observed the same sleepy, suburban scenery. His mind began to work out all the possibilities that could explain the predicament he was in. Nothing rational came to his mind, except for the potential of another Jamie-masterminded prank. *Jamie must be trying to do the prank of pranks on me. One prank to rule them all. What else can explain the suit and the big city projection?* he thought.

After a few minutes of pondering what to do next, Archer decided to play along. His plan was to bust through the door, charge down the stairs, and ruin whatever prank his sister was trying to pull. *That'll show her*, he thought.

The noise coming from outside of his room continued to intensify. "She must be getting impatient," he said, rubbing his hands together. "This is gonna be so good!" Archer walked over to his door and put his hand on the doorknob. "Here we go," he said with a wry smile. "Three…two…one—" Archer swung open the door and lunged forward. Rather than zooming down his home's stairs like he expected, Archer ran into a group of people and fell onto the sidewalk.

"Get out of my way!" he heard as people walked around him. Archer, shocked, did not move.

"Are you deaf, boy?" one man shouted. "I said get out of my way!" The man kicked Archer as he passed him.

Other people looked on but kept walking. Archer was afraid he would be stampeded by the enormous crowd of people.

"Hey, kid, get up or you're gonna get seriously hurt!" a voice said from behind him. He looked to see an outstretched hand. The intense, bright light coming from the person nearly blinded Archer. Archer quickly reached for the hand and was raised to his feet.

"Thank you so much," he said, "but where am—" Archer wasn't able to finish his sentence as the onrushing crowd swept the stranger away from him. Archer began walking on pace with the crowd and looked back to see that the door to his room was gone. In its place was a glass door connected to a building with big, bright neon letters spelling out the word CAREER. People were entering and exiting the building at a furious pace. "Weird," he said to himself.

Archer moved with the crowd as the CAREER building became a distant object. As he walked down the sidewalk, he saw that all the people were also wearing suits similar to the type he found in his closet. He looked down to see that his had the letters AFC sewn onto the chest. "Excuse me," he asked the person beside him, tugging at their sleeve.

"Buzz off, kid," he replied as he yanked his arm away from Archer.

"Geez Louise," Archer replied. "Take a chill pill, man."

Archer raised his head up and observed his surroundings. Two sidewalks flanked a busy street with many cars and buses, cruising in each direction with buildings lining both sides of the street as far as Archer could see. The front face of each building had flashing lights and neon signs on them, similar to the CAREER building. Archer was scared of the swarms of vultures he observed flying in between and above the buildings. It was all very peculiar to him.

He kept walking with the crowd and passed a building called FAME, another called JUSTICE, and another called FRIENDS. Next came a building called BASKETBALL. "Oh I've gotta go in that one," he told himself. Fighting the tide of the crowd, he made his way laterally to the front of the building. Inside the building, he could see a seemingly endless world of all things basketball. "Did I just find my ultimate happiness?"

As he was gazing inside the building, he was greeted by a man he immediately recognized. "Welcome! We're really glad to see you made it here," the man said.

"You're Eric Muncie!" Archer said in a starstruck tone. "I've seen every highlight tape ever made of you! You're the best point guard that the NBA has ever seen! I know all your moves! I can't believe I'm here talking to you, Mr. Muncie."

Eric laughed deeply and said, "You're right, my boy! But please, call me Eric. I'm here to assist you today," he said with a wink.

Archer understood the pun as he knew that Eric was the all-time leading assister in NBA history. "What an honor, Eric! I have so many questions to ask you."

"Fire away!" Eric said, jovially.

"Well," Archer said, "before I ask anything about basketball, I gotta ask, where am I and what am I doing here?"

Eric smiled and put his hand on Archer's shoulder. He extended his other arm to open the door. "Come in," Eric instructed. "Let's discuss this in my office."

The door behind them snapped shut as they entered. Archer then lost sight of Eric and saw what looked like a full-sized basketball court. As he walked forward, he heard a stadium announcer start speaking over the loudspeakers, "Ladies and gentleman, boys and girls! Get on your feet for the one, the only, ARCHERRRR COLEMANNNN!"

Suddenly, Archer found himself walking in the spotlight, on to an illuminated court in front of a roaring crowd, all chanting, "ARCHER! ARCHER!"

He looked around and waved at his adoring fans. The crowd raised their cheering to a deafening level as their hero acknowledged them. The cheers kept increasing in volume, the longer he waved. Archer loved it. The spotlight then dimmed, and the arena was pitch-black. The lights turned on, and Archer found himself in the lobby with Eric.

"Pretty cool, huh?"

"That was amazing!" Archer exclaimed. "Was that some kind of virtual reality experience?"

"Nope. That was the real deal. The court, the fans, the applause—all real."

"But how? Where did they all go?"

Eric chuckled and put his hand back on Archer's shoulder and said, "You've got a lot of questions, kid. Follow me this way." Eric led Archer past the reception desk to a seemingly never-ending hallway of rooms. Archer recognized the names on some of the doors as they passed by.

"Ja'kel Morgan! Barry Lord!" Archer said excitedly.

"That's right," Eric said. "We're all here!"

They reached Eric's door, and he ushered Archer in. Archer looked into the room with mouth agape and eyes wide open. Inside Eric's office were his basketball awards, game-worn memorabilia, and a TV screen playing highlights from his career. The spirit of the sport permeated every square inch of Eric's office. "I remember that game!" Archer said as he watched one of Eric's signature behind-the-back passes on the TV. "You had twenty points and thirteen assists in game seven of the championship series. I was about ten years old, and I remember it like it was yesterday!"

"Good memory, kid! That was one of my best games ever in the league," Eric replied.

Eric proceeded to sit behind his desk while Archer sat on the other side of the desk. "All right, kid," he began, "let's hear those questions."

"Where do I start?" Archer immediately responded.

"Wherever you want, kid! Is this your first time?" Eric asked.

"Yeah," Archer replied. "How did you know?"

"We'll call it a lucky guess," Eric said. "Now hit me with those questions."

Archer paused for a bit and asked, "Well, I guess, first things first: Where the heck am I? I feel like this all could be a dream, but it feels too real. I also thought I might have died and gone to some kind of afterlife, but I know that you're still alive so that can't be it."

Archer stopped like a deer in the headlights. "Wait a second," he said quickly, "you didn't die, did you, Eric? Please tell me you didn't die!"

Eric reassured him that he was, in fact, still alive.

"Phew," Archer said, swiping his forehead. "So if it's not a dream, and I'm not dead, where am I?" Archer asked.

"Archer, you're in a place not many kids like you get to come to," Eric replied. "You're in, what we like to call up here, 'the Marketplace.' Things are bought and sold here, just like any normal marketplace."

Archer interrupted, "But I can't buy anything. I left my wallet in my room."

"Well, you're in luck," Eric replied. "Things in the Marketplace aren't bought with money like you're used to. There's no need here."

Archer did not comprehend.

"Let me simplify it for you," Eric said. "If you noticed, each business has a name corresponding to the product they're selling. People come in because they're drawn to the product, just like you did here! You love basketball, so you came in wanting to check out what all we can offer you. Make sense?"

"Not really," Archer said with a look of confusion on his face. "What can you possibly offer me if I don't pay you anything in return for it?"

Eric looked him square in the eyes and said, "We offer the solution to every hope, dream, and desire you've ever had in your long sixteen years of existence. We can give you more than you've ever imagined basketball could ever give you! Just imagine it with me, kid! Happiness! Wealth! Meaning to your life!" Eric shouted. "We offer you the world, Archer!"

Archer, smiling ear to ear, couldn't contain his joy. "That's amazing! I want all those things! I'm in!"

"That's what I like to hear!" Eric shouted.

An awkward, quiet pause ensued.

"So," Archer said, "how do I get all of that if money isn't used here?"

"Ahh, here lies the brilliance of our package," Eric responded as he opened a drawer from his desk. He pulled out a piece of paper, handed it to Archer, and said, "All of the conditions of the deal are outlined here."

"You mean like a contract?" Archer asked.

Eric shook his head in disagreement. "No, no, no," he said adamantly. "It is much different than a contract. Contracts require something in return from the receiving party. We do not require anything from you! In fact, think of it less as a contract and more of a menu. I'll give it to you. You take a look at it and let me know what you want me to give you." Eric handed the paper to Archer.

The sheet was mostly empty with a title across the top that read Basketball: What Do You Desire from Us? Below were five options and a checkbox beside each one. The choices read:

- ☐ Meaning to your life
- ☐ Wealth
- ☐ Fame
- ☐ Acceptance
- ☐ Other _____

Below the final choice was a line for a signature.

"So what do you think?" Eric asked.

Archer looked up and said, "This all looks great."

"Perfect!" Eric exclaimed as he reached out to hand Archer a pen.

Archer grabbed it. "Yeah, this all looks great for sure," Archer said. "But I'm just a little confused because I've never had to sign a menu before."

Eric's countenance turned a little less friendly. "Don't you worry, kid. It's just so we can keep track of whose order is whose. Just check the boxes you want and sign it."

Archer looked down at the paper as he held it in his hands. He put the paper down on Eric's desk and checked the first, third, fourth, and fifth boxes. On the line of the "Other" choice, he wrote "Bring my family together."

"Attaboy, Archer," Eric said, affirmingly. "Now all I need you to do is sign."

Archer hesitated. Something stirred deep inside of him. He motioned the pen toward the paper to sign but stopped short.

"What's the holdup?" Eric asked sternly.

"I don't know," Archer replied with a blank stare.

Eric stood up. "Well, if you don't know, then just sign it!" he said as he tapped on the signature line.

Archer looked down at the sheet and then all around the room at the priceless memorabilia.

"All of this stuff is pretty cool, isn't it?" Eric asked coolly as he sat down again. "All of this and more will be yours if you just sign the paper!"

Archer heard what he said. He wanted to sign it. He wanted those things. He just couldn't get himself to sign it. "Can I have more time to think about this?" Archer asked. "What if I come back and sign later?"

"No can do, kid," Eric said. "We need you to join the team right now. Think about what you would miss out on between now and the next time you come back! And besides, you don't get to choose when you come back here once you leave. It can't be guaranteed that you'll ever be back. You need to sign the paper right now or else."

Archer began to feel irritated and said, "You know what, Eric, I can't believe I'm about to say this to you, but I don't like your tone! I can do whatever I want to do!"

Angered, Eric slammed his fist on the table and said, "Boy, you don't know who you're messing with! You have no authority here! You have no authority anywhere. You're a nobody, and you'll always be a nobody without us!" Eric stood up and pulled out a drawer from his filing cabinet, which contained manila folders. He ran his fingers through a row of them until he found the one he was looking for and pulled it out. He flicked it with his middle finger and tossed it on Archer's side of the desk. Archer took it and looked at the nametag on the folder. "Coleman, Archer," he read.

Archer looked up at Eric, frightened.

Eric continued, "We know everything about you, Archer Coleman. We know all your weaknesses. We know all your deepest, darkest secrets. We even know every thought you've ever had. It's all right there in your folder. You need us to fix your problems."

Archer flipped through the papers in the folder and, to his dismay, Eric was telling the truth. His whole life story was there, including thoughts and feelings Archer had not told anyone. Archer began to shake in fear as he put the folder back on the desk. He looked up at Eric, whose eyes appeared more sanguine than before. "What's it gonna be, kid?"

Archer stared at him for a little while before looking behind his back. The door was shut.

"Nice try, but there's no way out until you've signed the paper. You're trapped," Eric said with a sly smile.

Archer's heart sank. *Should I just sign it and get out of here?* he thought to himself. *He said there's no payment on my end. What would be the harm?* However, the uneasy feeling inside of him persisted. "Don't sign it," Archer heard. "Get up and leave right now."

But the door is locked. I can't get out of here. I'm stuck, he thought to himself.

"Trust me," Archer heard from deep inside of him.

Are you sure? he asked.

"Trust me," he heard again, clear as a bell.

Well, seems like the best option I've got at this point, he reasoned. *Here goes nothing.*

Archer sighed and took the pen in his hand and motioned it toward the paper as if to sign it.

"Good," Eric said. "I'm glad you've come to your senses."

Just as the pen was about to touch the paper, Archer threw the pen at Eric's face and made a mad dash to the door.

"Where are you going?" Eric yelled.

"I'm leaving this place, once and for all!" Archer yelled back as he braced for a collision with the door. To his surprise, he ran through the door with no resistance, as if it were not there at all. His momentum caused him to crash into the wall opposite Eric's office. Without thinking, Archer got up and sprinted toward the lobby.

"This is the biggest mistake you'll ever make in your pathetic excuse for a life!" Eric shouted. "You'll be back! Mark my words!"

"FAT CHANCE!" Archer screamed back to Eric as he sprinted through the hallway to the lobby. Archer zoomed by all the doors in the hallway as he ran faster than he's ever ran in his life.

"Have a nice day! We look forward to seeing you soon!" the receptionist said as he ran through the now-empty lobby.

"Not in a million years," he said under his breath as he reached for the door, only to find, just as with Eric's, he ran right through it at full speed. Archer fell to the ground in a heap. He braced himself in the fetal position to avoid being stampeded by the onrushing crowd of people. However, Archer did not feel any such stampede around him. Silence was the only thing that surrounded him.

After a few seconds, he felt the ground with his fingers and noticed it wasn't concrete, but rather it was soft like a blanket. Archer worked up the courage and opened one eye to take a peek at his surroundings. He was safely back in his bedroom.

CHAPTER 3

The Reveal

"Archer! Dinner is ready!" yelled a distant Jamie.

Night had fallen, and Archer's room was dark. He sat up and cautiously put one foot on the ground. It was solid ground, and he was indeed back in his room. With his heart still pounding, he stood up and flipped the switch to illuminate his bedroom. Archer looked around, and everything appeared normal. He walked to his closet and opened the door. Hangers hung with all his normal clothes. "Must've been a bad dream," he said, rubbing his eyes. Archer changed out of his school uniform and into a more comfortable outfit.

"ARCHER!" Jamie yelled louder. "Get down here so we can eat!"

"Okay, I'm coming!" he replied. "Give me a second! Sheesh!" Archer finished changing and put his ear up to the door to be sure he didn't hear anything strange on the other side. He heard normal household sounds and slowly opened the door. He peered through the crack and, to his delight, saw the normal hallway that led to the normal staircase that led down to the normal first floor. Archer swung the door open and walked downstairs where he saw his mother, Nicole, father, Henry, and Jamie sitting around the kitchen table.

"Geez, take long enough?" Jamie asked.

"Sorry, I took a nap. I guess I was more tired than I thought."

"Better late than never," Nicole said. "Good thing you woke up in time because we're having meatloaf with green beans and mashed potatoes. Your favorite!"

"Mmm, this is just what I needed," Archer said.

"I'm glad," Nicole said. "I figured a good meatloaf might be in order after what happened at school today."

Stunned a little bit, Archer looked at her. "What do you mean 'what happened at school today'?" Archer asked. "It was the last day of school. It's pretty much a national holiday!"

"Look, Mrs. Simpson told me about your little chat after—"

"She said she wouldn't!" Archer interrupted.

"Calm down, Archer," Nicole replied. "You're not in trouble. Look, your father, Jamie, and I were talking. We want to sit down and talk with you because we love you. We've all noticed that something is off, and we just want to help you."

The room was silent for a bit. Henry broke the silence. "Son, I understand it's hard to be a teenager. Believe it or not, I was your age once. I had questions. I had frustrations. But I never outright opposed authority like you're doing. I always listened to what I was told and respected whoever was in charge. We didn't raise you kids to be disrespectful. It's wrong, and it gives the family a bad name."

"Fine, I hear you," Archer replied with arms folded. "But I don't *try* to come across as disrespectful. All I ever do is ask questions, and people take it the wrong way! Also we are two completely different people. You're not me, and I'll never be like you, so stop comparing us. It's not fair."

No one spoke for a few seconds. Nicole broke the ice. "Archer, we just care about you. We wouldn't have even brought it up if this were a one-time occurrence. But your grades are slipping, your teachers are reporting misbehavior, and to top it all off, your sister tells us that you're questioning the validity of your HQ score. Now that really worries us because—"

"WHAT?" Archer blurted out. "Jamie, you told on me too? You said you wouldn't!"

"I'm sorry, Arch," Jamie replied, feeling guilty, "but I had to. This is serious, and you're my baby brother. I want you to get better."

Archer chuckled in disbelief. "'You want me to get better?' Like I'm someone with a disease that needs to be cured? Who do you think you are?" Archer pushed his chair back and stood up to leave the room.

Henry stood up as well to stop him. "Son, what Jamie's trying to say is that we love you and we want to help you feel better because you're obviously asking some deep questions right now. That's normal, but the manner in which you're doing it is unacceptable." Henry walked over to Archer and had him sit back down. "Look, after dinner, we're all going to sit down over there on the couch and just speak what's on our mind."

"You mean you want to have an intervention?" Archer asked facetiously.

"No, now, come on, Archer," Henry said. "This is serious. We're going to go through the importance of your HQ score. You should consider yourself lucky too. I'm going to be using information from work that not many kids your age have access to. I guarantee it will clear up a lot of issues you have by the end of it," Henry said.

"We'll see about that," Archer replied.

The family finished their meal and dropped their plates in the sink. Normally they would all help clean the dirty dishes before moving on to the next activity, but this was no normal evening.

"Archer," Henry said, "go ahead and take a seat on the couch. I'm gonna grab my laptop so I can pull up the presentation."

Archer did as he was told. While waiting for Henry, Archer checked his cell phone for any texts. *Eighteen new messages*! he thought to himself. *I've never gotten that many before*! Archer opened up the texting app to see what was happening. He was in a group chat with some of his friends. "Can't wait for the big party tonight!" one message read. "Party of the YEAR!" another read.

Oh no, Greyson's party! *I totally forgot*, Archer thought. Archer opened up his text thread with Ty. He had unread messages from him. "Still going to Greyson's?" "Archer! Hello!" "Earth to Archer! You alive, bro?"

Archer replied, "Yeah, I'm alive. LOL. Sorry, took long nap. I'll text u soon. Got some family stuff."

Nicole and Jamie came in the living room and sat on both sides of Archer as he put his phone back in his pocket. "Thanks for being cooperative. I know this isn't easy for you," Nicole told her son as she put her arm around him.

"You're welcome. It's not like I really had a choice, though," Archer replied. "You know," he said while stroking his chin, "I think what we really need right now is to let cooler heads prevail. I'm a little too emotional right now to have this talk and for it to *really* hit home. It's my fault, I know. But I just believe in the integrity of our family *so much*, and I wouldn't want things to get too out of hand. So you know what I'll do? I think I will just march myself right up those stairs and not come out until I've *really* thought about what I've done."

Archer began to stand up, but Nicole put her hand on his shoulder and forced him back down. "You're not going to Greyson's party tonight, Archer. Nice try," she said.

"How did you know about Greyson's party?" Archer asked.

"I'm the principal. I hear it all, honey," she said coyly.

Defiant, Archer said, "You know what, I don't care. It's not fair! Everyone that's anyone is gonna be there! I'm going, and that's final!" he said as he rose up again.

"Oh no, you are not," his father said as he entered the room. "Sit your keester right back down on that couch. THAT is final."

Knowing he was defeated, Archer did as his father told him and sat between his mother and sister.

Henry placed his laptop on the coffee table in front of the couch. He shared his screen with the TV so that the image on his laptop could now be viewed by everyone. "Great," Henry said as the TV lit up with the title screen of a presentation called "The Great Commission and You."

"Okey dokey. Like I said earlier, Arch, you are in for a real humdinger. My boss, Mr. Denis, has graciously allowed me to show you this short presentation we frequently show to new clients. Now, as you know, I'm an engineer at the Department of Worth. The Department of Worth," Henry said as he clicked to the next slide in the presentation, "began operation in our nation's capital, just down the road from this very house. It was the brainchild of some incredible intellectuals. Creating a government organization we now know as the DOW. At the time of its inception, the DOW was called the 'next great leap into the future of our nation.'"

Click. "On this slide, you can see a photo of the great men and women who worked tirelessly to create the DOW and its initial HQ score, which I will explain later. This panel was made up of the best and brightest scientific minds of their time, ranging from doctors to researchers to engineers to professors. All the sciences were represented. We call this panel the 'Freedom Fighters,' and their mission was named 'the Great Commission.'"

Click. Henry continued, "You may have already learned some of this briefly in elementary and middle school, but what you don't know yet is *why* this took place. One day, our leadership looked up and realized that our nation and its citizens were less happy, civilized, and fulfilled than at any time in our history. Our government decided 'enough is enough' and tasked the Freedom Fighters with uniting a divided nation."

On the slide, Archer could see pictures of buildings engulfed in flames and people shouting at one another, along with graphs showing the decline of mental and physical health over the decades, leading up to the foundation of the DOW.

Click. Henry pressed on. "The solution they came up with? The Happiness Quotient, aka the HQ that we all know and love. This novel technology was borne out of cutting-edge scientific knowledge. It was rudimentary and flawed, but it has been the job of the DOW to ensure that the HQ algorithms are constantly updated as the science improves by people like, ahem, yours truly," he said with a wink while pointing to himself. "The Freedom Fighters discovered that we all have more in common than we think. In short, they found that all we are is just a bunch of atoms and that we all share the same desire deep down inside of us: the desire to be happy. And the brilliance of the HQ is that it allowed our citizens to finally agree upon what was most important in life: being happy." Henry's smile could not have been bigger at this point. Archer's countenance did not reflect the enthusiasm of his father.

Click. "Now this slide is something that I am very proud to say that I have personally worked on."

Nicole nudged Archer with her elbow and whispered, "Listen up, Archer. This is where it gets really good!"

Archer folded his arms and slumped down further into the couch.

Henry continued, "These are the major factors that are taken into account when calculating a person's HQ. Believe it or not, they can be described with one phrase. This is what we call the 'Law of Outer Perception.' The Freedom Fighters discovered that the way people view you is a direct result of the happiness inside of you! Isn't that amazing! I mean, it just makes my head dizzy just thinking about it!" he said as he bounced his head back in forth and pretended to be dizzy.

Nicole and Jamie laughed along with Henry, but Archer found it cringeworthy.

Henry stopped his dizzy act and continued. "All joking aside," he said, clearing his throat, "Outer Perception works as the foundation of the HQ and our new society because people, on the whole, have this innate sense of right and wrong. We are able to calculate a person's HQ partially by aggregating the Outer Perception that those around them are receiving. This is why your daily surveys are so crucial to upholding the fabric of our society. We need constant data on the behaviors and emotions of those you encounter throughout the day, Archer. It's our glorious duty!" Henry said with a clenched fist raised to the sky.

Archer remained uninterested.

Henry cleared his throat again. "Now more objective factors are also included like net worth, IQ, house size, social media influence, career path, things of that nature, and each factor is weighted differently in our algorithm, of course."

Click. "I won't bore you with the details"—*Too late*, Archer thought—"about how Outer Perception is calculated, but your daily surveys play an integral role in the process, as I mentioned. Every citizen over the age of eight is legally required to complete their daily surveys at morning and at night. These surveys provide crucial information on the lives of the people you come into contact with, both in person and online. The DOW does not have an upper limit on the survey questions our citizens can complete each day, but we do mandate that each person answers at least ten questions per survey. That's only twenty questions per day. And we all know how quickly they take to complete, right? So everyone's survey results start to roll in, and they are thrown together in one big algorithmic pot and one, two, three, PRESTO! An HQ for each person is spit out, as well as a leaderboard showing how everyone's HQs stack up against everyone else's!" Henry could see that Archer was no less enthused than when the presentation started. He shook his head in disappointment.

Click. "All right," Henry said. "On this last slide, you can see the enormous positive benefits our country has experienced in the decades since implementing the HQ. This top graph shows downward trends in major public disagreements, high school and college dropout rates, crime and unemployment. Even unexpected indirect benefits like lower disease rates were observed. The bottom graph shows the major upward trends in national GDP, empathy toward other citizens, and average home size. When compared to nations that have not implemented this system, we see quite clearly that these trends are not observed there, thus proving that the Law of Outer Perception and the HQ system, as a whole, works brilliantly." *Click.* "The end."

Henry closed the presentation and his laptop. "So what do you think, Archer?" he asked triumphantly. "Any questions?"

Archer paused for a moment and said, "Yes, I do have a question. Can I go now?"

Jamie shook her head in disgust. "See! What did I tell you, Dad? He's not taking this seriously. I knew we should have taken him to DOW counseling! That'll really straighten him out. I mean, look at Adrian. There's no reason why Archer can't come around and be like—"

"BE LIKE WHAT?" Archer yelled. "Be like the good little robot that everyone wants me to be! I'm Archer Coleman! I'm not Henry Coleman! I'm not Adrian or Jamie Coleman! I'm Archer Coleman, and I will be doing what I want, when I want!" Archer shot up off the couch to go to his room, but his father intervened as he was almost to the staircase.

"Archer Coleman, you are not going anywhere until we get to the bottom of this! Your misbehavior is UNACCEPTABLE!" he screamed as he stressed each syllable. "Do you want to end up like Grandpa Franklin? Huh? Do ya?"

Archer froze in his tracks. He slowly turned around and looked his father directly in the face. "What did you just say?" he asked calmly.

"Uhhhh, which part?" Henry fumbled out. "The 'you are not going anywhere until we get to the bottom of this' part? Because we ARE going to get to the bottom of whatever is—"

Archer interrupted him, pointing his right index finger directly at his father. "You know perfectly well what part. What did you just say about Grandpa Franklin?"

Henry appeared at a loss for words.

Nicole stood up. "Oh, Henry! Why did you have to go and say that? He's not ready yet," she said with clenched teeth.

Archer advanced closer to his parents. "Mom. Dad. What is going on? What happened to Grandpa Franklin? You tell me, and you tell me right now."

Jamie turned back and saw tears rolling off her youngest brother's cheeks, onto the floor. Tears began to well up in her eyes.

Henry and Nicole glanced at each other and knew it was time. They sat down on the couch, and Henry patted the spot between him and Nicole. "Sit down, Arch."

Archer wiped his face and sat down next to his father. "Does everyone know but me?" Archer asked, still sniffling.

With sadness in their eyes, the other three nodded in agreement.

"I see," Archer said, feeling betrayed.

Henry put his arm around Archer. "Son, this talk was never going to be easy and, sometimes, we felt like it should have come sooner. But we saw just how much you looked up to your grandpa, and we didn't have the heart to tell you that he wasn't the man you thought he was." Henry paused to let the words soak in.

"Wha…what do you mean? Was he not really my grandpa?" Archer asked with a confused expression on his face.

"No, no, Franklin was your mother's father. He is your grandfather by blood. What I'm trying to say is—" Henry's voice trailed off as he tried to figure out a way to tell Archer without crushing him too much.

Nicole stepped in. "Honey, what your father is trying to say is that Franklin was not a good man. In fact, he was a criminal and a major threat to society. At one point, he was labeled by the government as the 'Most Wanted Man in America.'"

Archer didn't want to believe what he was hearing. He couldn't believe what he was hearing. It seemed so different than the wonderful, loving man he knew. Archer let the new information sink in for a moment. "Well," he finally said, "what did he do? Did he kill someone?"

"Worse," Nicole replied. "Your grandfather was the leader of an underground community seeking to overthrow and destroy everything that our society stands for. His heart burned with hatred, and his mind became fixated on anarchy. This transition from gentle man to evil terrorist happened at some point in his adult life. We still don't know exactly why or when this happened. It's still a mystery to us."

Archer thought about all the good times he had experienced with his grandfather. He began to question how he should feel about those memories. Were his words of affirmation to young Archer lies? Could anything he said be trusted now? Archer's heart ached. "What about this secret community?" Archer asked.

Henry answered, "Franklin was found guilty of kidnapping and committing treasonous acts toward the United States government and its citizens about fifteen years before you were born. The group he led called themselves the 'Truth Tellers,' in direct response to the Freedom Fighters. Their mission was to kidnap people, mostly children, in order to indoctrinate them with hate and misinformation about the new direction our nation was bravely headed. The goal was to create a large enough resistance to lead a coup that would overthrow the government and erase all the progress we've made in the past couple of centuries. It was, and still is, unfortunately, despicable," his father said as he shook his head in disgust.

"How come I've never heard of any of this?" Archer asked.

Nicole supplied the answer. "The court case was held under wraps to avoid the possibility of him being turned into an underground pop culture icon. He was sentenced to reeducation training and then a life of exile in the countryside, after they realized he was a hopeless cause. The court gave him no route to reenter into our modern civilization, including no means of communication with the outside world. In addition, surveillance cameras and microphones were installed on every square inch of the property to monitor his every move. He was to be a lowly producer of food, fiber, and fuel that would help keep alive the very society that he so wished to destroy. A very fitting punishment, if you ask me."

"Wait a minute," Archer said, "you let me hang around America's Most Wanted man as a young kid? You expect me to believe that?"

Henry answered, "It took about twenty years for him to earn back the ability to even see his grandkids in person. Your mother and I disagreed on when he could see you kids, but we eventually decided you all deserved to meet your grandfather. We never left you kids alone with him. I always had armed police buddies of mine come with us. We watched him like a hawk when he took you down to the pond to go fishing or into the barn to feed the animals. He knew that there were immediate repercussions if he tried any funny business."

"Well that's reassuring, I guess," said Archer. Archer did not know what to feel at that moment. Anger did not feel appropriate, although he felt like he should feel mad about what his grandfather had done. He was a criminal after all. A fleeting feeling of disbelief breached his mind, but he did not think his whole family would make up such an extravagant lie. They were too thorough with the details. A combination of disappointment and sadness could best describe how Archer's soul felt in that moment. Archer had ran out of questions to ask and stared blankly ahead.

"We understand this is a hard pill to swallow," Henry said as he patted his son on the back. "We knew from the first time you met your grandfather that a special bond existed between the two of you.

To be honest, your mother and I wished you would dislike Franklin so we wouldn't feel guilty about keeping you away from him. We feared that he would try and teach you lies that the Truth Tellers spew out, but, to his credit, he never did. Whether it was the reeducation training he went through or the constant surveillance, we'll never know. But your connection to Franklin made us realize it wasn't right to deprive you of that relationship, even with someone like him."

Nicole slid closer to Archer, and said softly, "I hope you can begin to understand the dilemma we found ourselves in. We chose to shield you from this information to protect you until we thought you could handle it. So, if the timing of the reveal was much too early or too late, we are sorry. Regardless, we are sorry that your grandfather was not the man you thought him to be."

Archer sighed, looked at his mother, and said, "It's okay, Mom."

Nicole and Archer hugged. She whispered in his ear, "We just love you and want you to be happy. Always know that." Nicole kissed her son on the cheek.

Without looking at his family, Archer stood up and said, "Good night, everyone," as he walked toward the staircase leading to his bedroom. Once in his bedroom, Archer fell face down on his bed and began to weep.

CHAPTER 4

Last First Day

"Move that desk a little to the left. Too far. Back to the right—perfect! Now everything is in its rightful place," Nicole said with her hands on hips and a smile on her face. "Ahh, isn't this just the most wonderful time of the year? Getting the school ready for classes feels just like putting the last presents under the tree!"

Archer disagreed. "The only good thing about tomorrow is that it's the last first day of school I'll ever have in this town. Sayonara, Morrison!"

Summer vacation had come and gone in a flash. Archer spent most of his time working his usual summer job at the local golf course where he worked on the grounds crew and played free golf in his spare time. As the weeks passed, Archer thought less and less about the conversation with his family concerning the Freedom Fighters, HQ, and his grandpa's criminal past. However, his family had convinced him to go to counseling sessions for his increasingly frequent outbursts of anger. Archer had also all but forgotten his experience with Eric Muncie by this time. Pool parties, late-night fast-food runs, and marathon video game sessions had overtaken his thoughts. Before he knew it, the time had come to start his senior year.

Although she knew it was best for Archer to go to college after graduating, Nicole was not looking forward to watching her youngest child leave the house. "But you'll miss me, right?" Nicole said jokingly to lighten her mood.

"Of course, I will, Mom! I'll even kinda miss Dad too," he said with a wink.

"I bet he'll even kinda miss you too," she said with a wink in return.

Archer laughed. "So are we done here?" he asked. "I've got a basketball, a hoop, and a driveway calling my name."

"Almost," Nicole said. "Just one more thing to do." Nicole walked over to her filing cabinet and opened the top drawer. She ran her fingers over the manila folders until she found what she was looking for. "Here it is," Nicole said as she pulled out an old-looking envelope and handed it to Archer.

"What's this?" he asked.

"This is the last letter your grandpa ever wrote to you."

Archer's eyes lit up. "He wrote me letters?"

"Well, to be honest," she said, "your grandpa wrote a few letters to all his grandkids. He had a lot of time on his hands, you know?"

Archer felt uneasy thinking about all the time a person must have without constant technology or people at their fingertips.

Nicole continued, "Your father and I screened each one before we gave them to you kids."

Archer thought for a moment and said, "I don't remember getting any letters from Grandpa. Was I just too young to remember?"

"No," Nicole replied, "your letters were far too complex for a child your age, so we burned them. It was the best way to get rid of any potential danger they posed. They contained what we thought were riddles and poems with strange symbols, and we were afraid he was trying to send secret Truth Teller messages to you."

"And Adrian and Jamie's letters were different?" Archer asked.

"Completely different," Nicole said. "Theirs were filled with questions you would expect from a normal grandpa. Like 'How is school going?' 'What sports are you into these days?' Those types of questions. But yours were so very strange. We just couldn't let you see them. Especially as a child."

"I see," Archer said. Archer was calm and collected, using his newly learned coping mechanisms from counseling. "I understand why you thought that might be the best mode of action," he said. "Why did you keep this letter then? And why keep it at school?"

"I kept it at school," Nicole explained, "because your father wanted me to burn it just like all the other ones, but I couldn't bring myself to do it. Something inside of me told me that keeping it was the right thing to do."

Archer looked at the envelope he was holding in his hand and began to internalize the importance of it. "I really appreciate you doing this for me, Mom. I'm still trying to process my thoughts and feelings toward Grandpa, so this is really special to have. Are you not worried it has Truth Teller propaganda?"

Nicole smiled. "There comes a time when every parent has to take their hands off their kids and let them ride the bike down the sidewalk by themselves. By doing this, we willingly allow our children to face challenges and get scraped up. The hardest part of parenting is sitting back and watching your kids fall, knowing full well that you could have prevented the pain. But that just stunts their future growth as an adult. That's where the IIQ comes in, I suppose, to reinforce those good behaviors that train a person not to fall off their bike anymore!"

This made sense to Archer.

"And now that you know the truth about Grandpa Franklin's criminal past and listened to your dad's presentation, I trust that you are able to discern truth from lie."

Archer appreciated being treated like an adult, for what felt like the first time in his life.

"And besides," Nicole added, "at the end of the day, he *was* my father. I have some very fond memories of the time we spent together when I was growing up. Grandpa Franklin was as honest and hardworking as any other adult in the community. He loved his family and instilled lessons in us that I still use to this day. I never would have imagined I was being raised by one of America's most dangerous threats to society."

"Wow, that's weird to think about, isn't it?" Archer asked.

"It really is," Nicole replied.

"I've racked my brain for decades, trying to figure out what went wrong," she said. "In fact, I blamed myself for a long, long time. I felt like I could have been a better daughter, and then he wouldn't have chosen to run away like he did." Nicole started to choke up.

Archer came over to his mother's side and put his arm around her. "How old were you when he ran away?"

"I had just turned thirteen when he told us he had to go. Dad sat us all down one night and explained that our safety was his top priority in this life. He always confused us when he said 'this life,' as if there was another one. Anyway, he said that leaving was the safest option for us. 'I can't explain it to you now, but hopefully, one day, I'll be able to. Just know that I love you all.' I can remember him telling us that like it was yesterday. Oh I cried and I cried and I cried every night for months."

Archer wiped a tear rolling down his mother's face. "I'm so sorry," Archer said. "What did Grandma Ruth think about it?"

"From what I know," Nicole replied, "Mom discovered his affiliation with the Truth Tellers after his arrest, which was five years after he had left us. I have no doubt she would have kicked his butt to the curb long before he left if she had known the truth. She was filled with indignation that her husband and father of her children had been working for a terrorist group right under her nose. 'Traitor! Exile him!' she would scream when someone would update her on the trial."

Archer was absorbed in the story and felt sadness for his mom. "So from age thirteen to eighteen, you didn't know where Grandpa was."

"That's right," she said. "He was a fugitive. I went through middle school and high school having to answer everyone's questions about my dad. There were always the rumors that he was a criminal on the run, but I deflected them as best I could to defend my dad's honor."

"That's a tough age," Archer interrupted.

"It sure was," Nicole said with a stressful chuckle. "But we knew nothing on his whereabouts or the reason why he left us, so I had no evidence to prove one way or the other. My heart was my only guiding light. That was until we found out that he had been caught. Government officials came to our house and informed us that Dad had been arrested for leading an underground group called the Truth Tellers that was kidnapping people and holding them hostage for the purpose of brainwashing them with anti-government rhetoric. I immediately ran to my room and screamed bloody murder in my pillow. The rumors were true."

Nicole looked up and noticed the clock. "Would you look at the time! It's almost four o'clock! We need to get home so I can get dinner started." Nicole blew her nose and dried up any remaining tears on her face. "With all that said, Archer, I trust you enough to have the letter and come to the right conclusions about its contents. I haven't read what's in it because I felt like you deserved one more private moment with your grandpa."

"Thanks, Mom," Archer said as they walked out of her office. "That means a lot." Archer debated with himself as to when he should read the letter. Part of him wanted to read it that same night, while another part wanted to wait until a later date. A final part of him wanted to burn the letter because he was afraid of the smut that the letter may contain. He was beginning to gain trust in his family and the HQ system he once decried. The last thing he wanted to do now was to be exposed to propaganda from his criminal grandfather that would place seeds of doubt in his brain. It felt good to be less rebellious.

By the end of summer vacation, he was able to control his emotions much easier, and he was much happier. He attributed this to his increased knowledge on the importance of the HQ. As a result, Archer felt closer to his family than he ever had. He even began to take steps toward increasing his HQ, like gaining more social media followers and working overtime at the golf course to earn more money. Watching his HQ rise was intoxicating, and he relished the conversations he and his family had about ways to increase their score.

Ultimately, Archer decided not to read his grandfather's letter. He was much happier living for his HQ score than he was at any other time in his life. He placed the letter in the shoebox under his bed for safekeeping. Maybe he would read it in the future, and maybe he wouldn't. However, Archer did not feel that burning it was the right thing to do. Archer felt at peace with the decision and slept well, knowing that tomorrow began the greatest year of his life: senior year.

The next morning, Archer pulled into Morrison High School's parking lot. Normally he would have had to fight for a decent parking spot, but seniors were given their own special area with plenty of room. "Pretty sweet, huh?" Archer asked Ty as he hopped out of his car. Ty and Archer parked next to each other almost every day of their high school career.

"Man, this year is going to rock," Ty said as they did their special handshake. "What are you looking forward to the most, Arch?"

"You know," Archer said, "I think I'm most looking forward to Mr. Locke's philosophy class."

Ty stopped in his tracks. "Are you serious? Think about it, Arch!" Ty implored. "The basketball season! The parties! I mean, you did miss the party of the century at Greyson's this summer, but I'm sure there will be some other great ones!"

"Don't remind me," Archer said. "Those all sound awesome, but I just feel like philosophy is going to be so important for us as citizens. Jamie told me it would be life-changing, and what could be more exciting than that?"

Ty stood still again. "Man, you really changed this summer. I feel like I don't know you anymore," he said. "Don't get me wrong, I like the new you! But this came out of nowhere."

Archer hadn't told Ty about his vision with Eric Muncie or any of the information regarding his grandfather, including the letter. Archer just shrugged his shoulders and said, "I'm not sure either, but I like the new me too."

The boys marched inside school in their uniforms with the rest of the students.

"Welcome to philosophy class, seniors," Mr. Locke proudly announced. "A perfect way to start the day, I'm sure all of you are thinking! Now, since today is only a half day, we don't have much time together. So without further ado," he said, holding up a piece of paper, "your first assignment."

Some students in the class groaned.

"Already?" one student mumbled.

"Quiet down, class," Mr. Locke said. "This is just a prequiz that we always give out on the first day. It will not be graded, so don't worry," he said as he walked up and down the rows, handing out the survey. "We just want to collect good data on your knowledge of how things operate before and after taking the course. Every class is always so amazed at how much they've learned in just one school year!"

The class became quieter and quieter as they all began to scribble their answers.

Archer, sitting near the front, was excited to show off how much more he knew than his classmates. He wrote his name at the top and looked at the quiz. It had five questions.

(1) Who was the greatest Freedom Fighter, and why?

Archer thought about his father's presentation but didn't remember him going into the details about any particular names. He left this question blank. "Oh for one. All right, we'll get the next one," Archer said under his breath.

(2) What is the most heavily weighted variable in the HQ equation?

With confidence, Archer wrote "Outer Perception" on the answer line.

(3) What is religion?

Religion? he thought to himself. *I know I've heard that word before, but I just can't put my finger on it.* He wrote "The study of the brain" on the answer line.

(4) Under which president was the Department of Wealth created?

Archer did not know, but he wrote down "Miller" on the answer line as his dad always spoke about President Miller and how brilliant he was.

(5) What is the meaning of life?

This question caught Archer off guard. He had never considered what the meaning of his life was. After some thought, he put "Happiness" on the answer line.

After ten minutes had passed, Mr. Locke broke the silence. "All right, class! Time's up! Pass your quiz to the person in front of you, and I will collect them and grade them this evening." Mr. Locke gathered all of the quizzes and placed the stack on his desk. "Now I don't want to disparage any of the other classes or teachers in the building, but I'm going to let you all in on a little secret." Mr. Locke was an animated man, and he leaned in toward the class exaggeratedly. "This class, senior philosophy, is the most important class of your whole high school career. More important than algebra. More important than chemistry. Even more important than lunch!" The class laughed, and Mr. Locke knew he had his audience sitting on the edge of their seats. "The reason I can confidently say that is because our government says so. Here, I'll prove it!" Mr. Locke walked behind his desk and pulled up a video on his computer that was projected onto the front screen for the whole class to see.

The video began with a shot of the president sitting behind her desk in the Oval Office. "Hello, seniors. Welcome to philosophy class. This class is designed to give you an in-depth look into how our modern world was shaped, and which systems we created to give it that shape. You will delve into the past to learn about a time in our nation's history when hatred and bigotry ran amok, and you will learn about the brave heroes and heroines that dedicated their lives to creating a more happy and equitable society. This class is the most important class you will take in your high school career."

Mr. Locke paused the video and pointed to the screen, jumping up and down, saying, "See! Told ya so! Told ya so!" He hit the play button on the video.

The president continued, "Please pay attention to the instruction of your teachers as this material will help you become happy citizens and productive members of our great society. Our happiness is at stake. Thank you and enjoy your senior year."

"Wasn't that amazing?" Mr. Locke asked as he exited out of the video.

The class agreed.

"Wasn't that inspiring?"

"Yeah!" said some in the class.

"Doesn't that just make you want to crack open your textbooks and read chapter 1 by tomorrow?"

"Yeah!" said only one person in the class.

The whole room looked at Archer.

Mr. Locke shook his head in approval and said, "That's what I'm talkin' about, Archer! I love the enthusiasm! Class, you could learn a thing or two from Mr. Coleman!"

Archer smiled and felt a sense of pride.

Mr. Locke continued, "Yes, class. Tonight you are to read chapter 1 in your textbook, answer the questions at the end of the chapter, and we will discuss it tomorrow. I have no doubt that you will all find it a fascinating read."

The school buzz went off, and the doors slipped open. Archer packed his backpack and headed to his next class with Ty.

"Wasn't that incredible?" Archer asked.

"Yeah," Ty replied, "it really was. Aren't you a little embarrassed though that you cheered for *homework*?"

Archer laughed and said, "I guess a little. The excitement kinda took over my body, and I couldn't help myself!" Just as he had finished his sentence, Archer heard a voice from behind him.

"Yeah, Archer, what the heck, man? You're making us all look bad!"

Archer looked back to see who said that to him. "Oh hey, Grace. I didn't mean to—"

43

Grace laughed and slapped him on the shoulder. "I'm just giving you a hard time, Archer. Well, I'll see you around! Gotta get to class!"

"See ya!" the boys said in unison. The boys looked at each other, a bit shocked. They began to walk toward their next class.

"Did that really happen?" Archer asked.

Ty nodded his head up and down. Archer let out a big sigh as a smile appeared on his face. "Wow," he said. "I…can't…believe it!" he exclaimed. He jumped up and hugged Ty.

"Be cool, Archer. People are watching!"

"I don't care!" Archer said. "All these years I've been trying to get Grace to notice me, and then BAM! Out of the blue, she starts talking to me! What do you think it means? What should I do? Should I text her? You of all people know how long I've been waiting for something like that to happen. This is the best day ever!"

"Easy, Archer," Ty said. "Calm down a bit. I'm sure she was just trying to make you feel better after you embarrassed yourself in class. That's the kind of girl she is."

"Oh, I know, Ty. She's the nicest girl in school. But come on! She went directly out of her way to talk to me. That's gotta be something, right?"

"Maybe," Ty said, "but maybe not. Could be nothing. I wouldn't get my hopes up."

Archer shoved Ty. "Come on, man! Let a guy dream a little bit!"

Ty laughed. "Hey, I'm just trying to protect you, man. You know how girls are."

Suddenly an announcement came over the speakers. "ONE MINUTE UNTIL CLASS. I REPEAT. ONE MINUTE UNTIL CLASS."

Ty looked at Archer and said, "This is where we split, Arch. I gotta get to gym. Where are you headed?"

"Uhh, let's see," Archer said as he opened up a folded paper with his schedule printed on it. "I'm going to calculus. Gross."

"All right, man, adios," Ty said as they went their separate ways.

"See ya later, Ty," Archer said.

Archer replayed the interaction with Grace over and over in his head throughout the day. *What do I do now?* he kept thinking to himself. *I could just send her a friendly text asking how her first day went. Yeah, that would be good!* However, another thought popped in his head, as if from a completely different person. *Hold on a second. What if she takes that as flirting, and she doesn't think of you like a potential boyfriend? For one, that would be embarrassing and, secondly, it would make it super awkward between you two, and she would never talk to you again!* The more optimistic voice chimed in, *But it's* senior *year. As in, everyone goes their separate ways in a few months. We could never see each other again! You can't win the lottery if you don't buy a ticket! Send the text.*

Don't do it, said the other voice, *She'll probably be weirded out and tell all her friends how creepy you are. It'll only lead to heartbreak and embarrassment. Do not do it.*

The debate in Archer's mind captivated his thoughts much more than the subjects being taught in class that day. Before he knew it, his first day of school was over, and he was back at home, eating dinner with his parents. Jamie had since returned to New York City to resume her pursuit of an acting career. "Earth to Archer," his mother said.

"Huh? Did you say something, Mom?" Archer asked.

Nicole chuckled. "Yes, honey. I asked how your first day went. It's like you've been under some kind of spell, since you got home!"

"I think I'm just tired from all the classes today. Sorry about that," he said as he ate a bite of food. "The first day was okay. I think I'll learn a lot this year, and I'm super excited about philosophy class. We've already got homework, but I'm actually looking forward to it."

Henry looked impressed. "Wow, son! I'm really glad you feel that way. Most kids don't realize how great that course is until later in the year. You're gonna ace it, no doubt."

Archer smiled and felt a sense of warmth in his body from his father's words of encouragement.

"And hey, who knows? Maybe it'll spur you on to go to college to be an HQ engineer like your old man!" Henry added.

"Let's not get ahead of ourselves," Archer replied.

Once dinner was over, Archer excused himself to his room to do his philosophy homework. He sat down at his desk and opened the thick textbook to chapter 1, titled "The Fight for Freedom." Archer excitedly pored over the text and answered the questions in his notebook. Once finished, he could barely get to sleep as his mind raced with excitement about what he was going to learn tomorrow in class.

Archer woke up the next day, just as excited and completed his morning routine of eating breakfast and getting dressed. He drove to school and walked straight to his first period class like a man on a mission.

"Pass around the basket, please!" Mr. Locke told his class. "Tear the assignment out of your notebooks, and place it in the basket when it comes to you. No messing around today! We've got a lot to cover in this class, and we don't want to get behind!"

Archer tore out his answers and placed the paper in the basket. As he turned back to pass it, he caught Grace's eyes, who happened to be sitting right behind him. "Oh, pardon me," Archer said, tossing the basket at her and quickly turning around. A look of bafflement came across Grace's face, but she did not say anything. Archer felt a bomb go off in the pit of his stomach. *I blew it*, he thought. *It's over before it started. She must think I'm the biggest weirdo in the world.* Archer put his face in his hands and groveled a bit longer. *Well, on the bright side, now I can put my whole focus into school!* he finally thought to cheer himself up. Archer removed his face from his hands and sat up, nice and straight.

"Is this everyone's homework?" Mr. Locke asked as he grabbed the papers from the basket.

Everyone nodded their heads, and he placed the stack in a drawer on his desk. He proceeded to open a presentation on his computer that was projected onto the front screen. Archer's problem with Grace receded to the back of his mind as he read the title slide, "Chapter 1: The Fight for Freedom."

"Did everyone find last night's reading interesting?" Mr. Locke asked the class.

Some in the class nodded.

"Good. Did anyone find it particularly interesting and would like to share some insights they gained from it? Maybe Archer, seeing as you were so enthused yesterday?"

Archer could feel the blood race to his cheeks. He sat up a little straighter and said, "Uhh, I'd say that the whole chapter was very insightful, and I'm real excited to hear you explain it more in-depth for the class."

Mr. Locke clapped his hands together. "Thank you, Mr. Coleman, that is very kind. Anyone else? Oh, yes! Ms. Meyers, what would you like to share?"

Archer listened intently to Grace's answer. "What I enjoyed most was learning more about our nation's pre-HQ time. Up to this point, we hadn't learned a whole lot about this dark period in our nation's past. I feel sad that it's a part of our history, but I am so happy that we figured it out and turned the fate of our whole country around."

Mr. Locke smiled. "A wonderful answer! What a perfect segue into the lesson at hand."

Archer fell a little more in love with Grace after hearing her shared enthusiasm for the chapter.

"As Ms. Meyers so eloquently mentioned," Mr. Locke said, "our nation was not always the pinnacle of fairness and equality we find it to be today. Once upon a time, our great nation was guided by the exact opposite principles of fairness and equality. Slavery was the law of the land. Slavery is where one person takes the rights away from another human and uses that person for whatever purpose the master so chooses. In this society, humans were brought to work on their farms with no pay and no way of regaining their freedom. Farms, as you may recall, are the places where our food, fiber, and fuel are grown. Back in those days, most families produced what they ate themselves. We had not yet freed our society from the scourge of the agrarian lifestyle." Mr. Locke was pacing back and forth in the front of the class with his hands behind his back as he lectured.

He continued, "Families were often ripped apart from each other. Children never saw their parents again. Husbands never saw their wives again. It is just sickening to think about. Thankfully, we had a great war to end this awful slavery system. The side fighting to end slavery won the so-called 'Civil War,' and the slaves were officially set free. But what does 'free' mean? How does one define the term *freedom*? This is a recurring topic of the course."

Archer was furiously taking notes in his notebook. He was enthralled by the presentation.

"The freeing of slaves, I will argue, did not result in true freedom for this group of people. While it was now illegal to own other human beings, and former slaves were set free, they were often offered no place to go. Even worse, discrimination against this group of people was codified into the law of the nation."

Archer raised his hand and was called upon. "What type of discrimination was allowed?" he asked.

"Good question," Mr. Locke replied. "Many forms of discrimination were allowed, including the separation of schools children could attend, the types of restaurants people could eat at, and the types of bathrooms they could use. They were not even allowed to drink from the same water fountain as everybody else."

The class was in shock as they had not yet been taught this awful stain on the United States' history.

"Does anyone have any idea why these people were discriminated against?"

The class was silent as students tried to reason how a person could treat another person in this manner.

One student asked, "Was it because they were traitors to the nation?"

"A good guess, but no," Mr. Locke said. "These people were brought in from faraway lands. They were not even citizens of this country to begin with."

Another student raised their hand and asked, "Could it be that these people were unproductive members of society and that was the only way they could contribute?"

Mr. Locke replied, "This may be what masters of the time thought, but it is still not the correct. In fact, the reason had nothing to do with anything they could control. They were made slaves based solely on the tint of their skin."

An audible gasp was let out by several students.

"That's right, class. The great crime that these people committed was that their skin contained much more of the pigment melanin than the masters' skin."

Archer felt an intense sadness upon hearing this new information. He raised his hand again and asked, "How could someone possibly believe that a person with darker skin deserves slavery?"

Mr. Locke stopped his pacing and looked at Archer. "The answer to this lies in the fact that they believed these people were not people at all."

Archer again asked, "How could that possibly be?"

"Now we are beginning to get into the philosophical side of things," Mr. Locke said. "These slaveholders reasoned that people of a certain skin color were subhuman and not worthy of being treated like full human beings. These slaves were treated like farm animals," Mr. Locke paused.

He continued, "Now we all have thoughts and beliefs based on many different variables, such as our upbringing, our education, and our friend groups. Back then, the guiding force for thoughts and beliefs of the time was what is called *religion*, a word no one was able to define correctly on our quiz yesterday. 'A mental disorder' was the closest and most humorous response. Religion is the belief in the supernatural, which, by definition, does not exist. Science has not shown one shred of evidence that a world outside of this one exists. And back in pre-HQ days, fairy tales and myths were recorded in 'religious' texts, and groups of people believed their stories to be true."

Some in the class began to chuckle at the simplemindedness of these people.

Mr. Locke chuckled as well and said, "I know it sounds silly today, but it is indeed true! They used the morals from these myth books to write laws and justify atrocities like slavery and war. Aren't we blessed to live in a time where this is not the case?"

Many in the class nodded their heads in agreement.

A student in the back raised their hand and asked, "When did these things happen? I noticed that years weren't given for any of these events?"

Mr. Locke replied, "The Freedom Fighters and government officials of the time correctly decided that it would be best not to mention such dates. Time was reset at the moment we codified the HQ system because they realized our nation had resurrected, which means to come back to life from the dead. The old nation was dead, and a newer, better one had emerged from it. While there is technically no pre- and post-United States of America, we became a completely new nation, unrecognizable from the first."

This answer made sense to all the students, and no further questions were asked.

"All right class, this topic was pretty heavy, so I want to wrap this lesson up by sharing some good news," Mr. Locke announced to the class. "Starting this year, students will be eligible to earn bonus HQ points by attending and completing this philosophy course."

The students looked excitedly at one another.

"That's right!" he exclaimed. "This class has been deemed so crucial to your education that your HQ will see a significant bump up each semester, if you make attendance and scoring high on tests a priority in your busy lives. Something to think about!"

The school buzz went off, and the door slid open, just as he had finished. "Have a great day, class!"

Archer packed up his things and exited the room, wishing that class did not have to end.

CHAPTER 5

Deeper Down the Rabbit Hole

The first half of the school year went well, by Archer's standards, as he received all As in his classes and was named captain of the basketball team. Archer tried hard and paid attention in all his classes, but philosophy was by far his favorite. He found himself mentally replaying the daily lessons throughout the day and into the evening. Archer never missed a homework assignment and read ahead in the textbook, something he had never done for any class. The topic was incredibly fascinating to him. Not only were the lessons stimulating intellectually, they were also beginning to help him feel whole. His deepest questions about existence were starting to be answered. The HQ system began to make more sense. He felt an intense pride in his score and began to do all he could to raise it.

Over the coming months, he worked mightily at increasing his social media presence and raising his GPA so he could graduate at the top of his class. He also began to seriously consider what he was going to do once he graduated high school. Archer researched majors and schools that have the biggest impact on a person's HQ score. He discovered through conversations with Mr. Locke that majoring in philosophy resulted in a major HQ bump, as acquiring this degree often led to a good paying, highly influential job. He began filling out scholarships to the best colleges with a philosophy major that he believed he could get accepted into.

On the first day of the spring semester, Archer found himself back in the front row of Mr. Locke's classroom, soaking up the daily lesson like a dry sponge under a running faucet.

"Hello, class!" Mr. Locke exclaimed. "Welcome back from winter break. I hope you're all feeling recharged and ready to end your high school careers on a high note!"

Various students in the class nodded their head in agreement.

He continued, "I also want to congratulate those of you who received a generous increase in their HQ from being in the top 10 percent of performers in the class."

Archer smiled as he recently discovered he was the top philosophy performer in all of Morrison High and received the hefty HQ bump, which moved him up 0.1 percent of a percentile.

"Now the first half of this class was designed to introduce a pre-HQ America rampant with hatred, bigotry, and division. Its foundation was built upon these principles. In other words, you now understand *why* our nation needed rebuilt from the ground up," Mr. Locke said. "I will now be using the second half of the year to teach you *how* America fixed its problem and *how* we rebuilt. And yes, I know what you're all thinking. The HQ system is the major solution that has corrected the issues we discussed in the first semester."

Mr. Locke struck his usual pose of folded hands behind his back and a slow pacing back and forth in the front of the class. "How was the HQ introduced?" he asked rhetorically. "That story begins with the election of President Xavier C. Miller. This great man inherited a country in crisis and promised on the campaign trail to unite our citizens. Once in office, President Miller arranged for the largest convention of scientific minds that had ever been seen. We call this convention 'The Great Commission' and the people involved 'Freedom Fighters.'"

The furious scribbling of pencils on notebook paper could be heard as students tried to keep up with the pace of the lesson.

Mr. Locke continued, "This giant committee of scientists and intellects gathered to determine what stability and satisfaction are and how a human best attains them. They looked at the latest findings in neuroscience, psychology, and sociology to determine what makes a human and a society happy. They sought answers to the difficult questions such as 'what can be done to ensure that there is no more war between differing people groups?' And 'how do we maximize pleasure and minimize pain in the lives of our citizens?' The brilliant solution they came to was this: create one perceived people group." Mr. Locke paused to let the words sink into the minds of the students.

"It was that simple," he added. "Create one nation, one people, one tribe in the minds of the citizens. Delete division among them, and war would cease to exist."

Archer stopped writing to think about what this means. He was very confused and raised his hand.

"Yes, Archer," said Mr. Locke.

"How could they possibly make a whole population of people not see differences anymore?" Archer asked, "It seems impossible."

Mr. Locke agreed. "Indeed it does. But look around you. Our society today is living proof that they were able to accomplish this task. Allow me to explain how they achieved the impossible." Mr. Locke walked to the whiteboard and drew two lines: one continuous horizontal line and one with many small dashed vertical lines next to each other.

"Think of the points on these two lines as the citizens of America," Mr. Locke instructed. "Our old system was like the small series of vertical lines. Our citizens were not connected. They did not have one common factor that held them together. People of old believed in different value systems, and their individual value systems inevitably led to feelings of superiority." Just as he had said this, a hand shot up in the air. "Yes, Grace," said Mr. Locke.

"Doesn't the HQ system create a sense of superiority and division as well? It's all based on ranking."

Mr. Locke looked at her for a moment. "Another fine question, Ms. Meyers," he replied. "This very concern was deeply debated by the Freedom Fighters." He began pacing again and continued, "After poring over the data, they concluded that personal growth and personal happiness were paramount qualities of a successful life. They realized not everyone at the time was trying to achieve physical success. Many still believed in the mythical religions of old with their value systems based on the supernatural that taught them to store up their riches in an afterlife, which we know doesn't exist. This observation helped guide them through the development of the HQ score to incentivize people to follow physical success. By doing this, each citizen was now aiming at the same target. They were all playing by the same rules of the same game. *This* is what destroyed the sense of superiority and division among us. Just brilliant," he said with reverence.

Archer felt a deep sense of joy inside him that manifested itself through a smile on his face.

Mr. Locke caught sight of this and smiled himself. He continued, "This all makes intuitive sense. Think about it: the more successful people there are in a society, the more society benefits. Conversely, this creates fewer unsuccessful drains on society. The HQ system guides people and societies toward unity and success. Unity and success lead to fewer conflicts in a society.

"But how does this unity and success create happiness? It isn't called the *happiness* quotient for nothing. Happiness, as the data clearly shows, lies in striving for excellence, materialism, individual freedom, liberty, democracy, eradication of pain, eradication of disease, eradication of judgment and, most importantly, allegiance to a system that provides community, shelter, and togetherness. All these variables are factored into the HQ algorithm developed by the Freedom Fighters and by ascribing to this system, we are all happy brothers and sisters of the same citizenship. This creates an enormous sense of belonging, which is a desire in each and every human heart."

Archer began to tear up because this was exactly how he felt working toward increasing his HQ. He had never been able to put this feeling into words, but he now realized that he desired to belong to something bigger than himself. Playing basketball for his school gave him a taste of this feeling, but belonging to a nationwide system provided a sense of belonging like he had never experienced. He felt intense gratitude for the Great Commission, the Freedom Fighters, and the HQ system.

The school buzz went off, and Archer exchanged a smile and a head nod with Mr. Locke as he headed out the door to his next class. Archer had never felt a strong bond to the leaders of his nation or any authority figure, for that matter, in his seventeen years of existence. However, he increasingly welled up with patriotism toward his country and its leaders as the spring semester progressed. *How could I not?* he thought to himself, considering all the work and intentionality that had gone into creating this wonderfully designed HQ system. *Where would the nation be right now if it weren't for their heroics?* he often pondered. *Nowhere good. That's for sure.*

The Freedom Fighters and President Miller saved this nation in Archer's mind, and the HQ system had gained the status of a benevolent father, always looking out for Archer's best interest. It punished him for doing bad and rewarded him for doing good, just like a loving father does. He also felt sick to his stomach thinking about the savagery that must ensue in places around the world not blessed to have such a system of checks and balances on its citizens.

One early spring afternoon, after the basketball season had ended, Archer found himself driving alone in the countryside. He had much more free time to do whatever he wanted with no more sports to worry about. He used these drives to clear his mind of distractions and ponder his life's trajectory. Being the captain of the team had earned him valuable HQ points, mostly from popularity and jealousy of his peers, so he was thankful for the experience. However, that chapter of his life was over, and it was time to think about additional ways to increase his HQ score. The most effective manner in which to increase his score, he reckoned, was to get accepted into one of the philosophy programs he applied to.

Archer had applied to over fifteen universities that offered a philosophy program, but he had not been accepted by a single one yet. In fact, he had already been rejected by eleven of them. The deadline to get accepted was quickly approaching, and Archer was very nervous because he did not have any backup plans. Although the rejection letters dropped his HQ score a couple of points, he mitigated the damage by keeping this information to himself so his classmates could not know about his failures and downvote him on their daily surveys. "We're down to the final four. There's still hope," he said to himself. "Help me out, HQ, I'm doing this for you."

After an hour of driving in the countryside, Archer decided to come home so he could check the mailbox for an acceptance letter, just as he had done every day now for weeks. "Let's see what we have in here today," he said as he opened the mailbox. Three envelopes and a magazine were stacked on top of one another. "Come on, baby. I feel it. Today's the day!" he exclaimed. Archer picked up the stack. "Bill, bill…hey! All right! My new *Good HQ-Keeping* magazine came in!" he said excitedly. He flipped through it back to front, reading the titles of the articles: "5 Hot Tips Guaranteed to Increase Your HQ Score this Summer." "Here's Everything You Need to Know About the Algorithm."

"Oh man," Archer said aloud, "this is a juicy one!" Archer had momentarily forgotten about his lack of an acceptance letter. Reading one of the articles, Archer walked inside his house and found his parents standing in the entrance to greet him. "Uhh, can I help you?" Archer asked.

Henry and Nicole stood there, smiling. "What's going on? You guys are acting all weird," he said.

Nicole walked toward Archer and hugged him. "Here, take a look at this," she said as she handed Archer an opened envelope.

His heart leapt. "Is this what I think it is?" he asked.

Teary eyed, Nicole furiously nodded her head up and down.

Archer looked at the envelope. "First off, excuse you for opening my mail," he said jokingly. "Second, this is incredible! I was really starting to think no one would accept me."

Henry came forward and patted his son on the back. "Truth be told, your mom and I were getting a little worried ourselves. Think about the score hit I would've taken if word got out that an HQ engineer's son couldn't get into college! Ha! Dodged a bullet there!"

Archer agreed. "Well, take a look at it already!" Henry told his son.

"Okay! Okay!" Archer said as he unfolded the paper.

He began to read the letter aloud, "Mr. Coleman, We are delighted to announce your acceptance into the School of Social Engineering at Helmuth University. Many of our nation's greatest HQ influencers have graced the very halls and classrooms you are to set foot in. This is a particularly exciting time to attend Helmuth University as you will have opportunities that most people your age can only dream about. We encourage you to make this acceptance letter publicly known so that you may receive a large increase in your HQ score, as many of your peers have no doubt applied to our prestigious program. To accept our offer, please visit the website listed below. We look forward to seeing you this fall. Congratulations, Helmuth U." Archer jumped up and down with his parents in excitement. "Helmuth was my number one choice! This is the best day of my life!"

The three of them hugged and migrated on to the living room couch. "Oh, honey!" Nicole exclaimed. "We are just so proud of the improvements you've made since our big talk last summer! Watching your child's score skyrocket is one of the proudest moments in a parent's life, isn't it, Henry?"

"Sure is," he replied. "The points we get for our score isn't too bad either! Speaking of, Archer, you need to post about this! Let everyone know!"

Archer hugged his parents one more time and ran off to his room to write the perfect post for his friends and followers. Archer took off his backpack and sat down at his desk. He took a picture of the letter with his phone at the perfect angle and the perfect lighting for it to be uploaded to his social media pages. "Now what should the caption be?" he asked himself. "I'll keep it simple," he decided.

After two hours of great consternation, he finally settled on a caption: "Helmuth U! See U in the Fall!" Archer felt satisfied and posted to his accounts. Dopamine rushed to his brain with every *DING* that rang out from his phone. The likes and comments on his posts were overwhelmingly positive and made Archer feel very good about himself. Archer's eyes were glued to his phone for the next couple hours. A few of his friends even texted him personally to congratulate him and ask about the specific program he got accepted into. "I don't think this day could get any better," he said aloud as he flopped onto his bed. Just as he said this, a loud *DING* came from his phone. He checked to see what it was. "Text from Grace Meyers."

Millions of monarch butterflies began to flap their wings in his stomach. He opened the text and read it, "Congrats, Arch! I just knew you'd go somewhere awesome like Helmuth. You're way too smart not to. I'm so happy for you! See you tomorrow!"

"Okay, *now* it can't get any better," he said. Archer typed and edited a response for forty minutes until he settled on what was to him, the perfect message: "LOL. Thanks so much! See u tomorrow!" Archer laid supine on his bed and waited for a response back from Grace. However, none came. The longer he waited, the sleepier he became. The adrenaline of the afternoon was finally wearing off. In addition, the time between each new like or comment to his posts grew longer and longer.

The grip on his phone slowly loosened as he fell asleep with a large grin on his face. Archer's phone began to slowly slide down the left side of his body until it fell off the edge of the bed where it made a loud *THUD*! Archer's eyes opened at once. "Must have dozed off," he told himself as he reached down to grab his phone. Archer immediately pulled his hand away from the floor. His hand had submerged in freezing cold water. "What in the world?" he asked. He looked over the edge of the bed and saw his phone floating on top of dark, choppy waters. Archer scooted toward the middle of the bed and looked around to find himself in the middle of an ocean of water with no land in sight. He and his bed were bobbing up and down on top of the waves.

Archer realized that it was dusk, and nighttime was quickly approaching. His need to grab his phone to have a light and call someone was paramount. Luckily, his phone was surrounded by a waterproof case, so he knew it wasn't ruined. He looked in the water and saw his phone floating about a yard from his bed-boat.

Archer reached as far as he could, but the phone was just out of his reach. He tried to paddle the water to force the phone closer to him, but this was to no avail. Archer grabbed on to the mattress as he stretched further, but the device was still an inch out of his reach. He made one more mighty lunge until he felt the phone in his grasp. "Gotcha!" he yelled. At that moment, a large gust of wind pushed against Archer's back, and he lost his grip of the mattress, causing him to plunge into the water. The shock of the cold stunned Archer. His body tensed, and he was struggling to breathe. Archer had very little experience swimming in pools, let alone open water.

"HELP! SOMEBODY HELP ME!" Archer yelled at the top of his lungs. "PLEASE, ANYBODY!" The wind continued to howl as nighttime had fully descended. He could no longer see his hand in front of his face. The intensified waves began to pull him under. "HEEEEEEELLLLLLPPPPP!" he screamed as his head submerged underwater. Archer shot upward for a much-needed breath of air only to be immediately smacked in the head by a powerful wave. Disoriented, he drifted down into the depths of the pitch black waters. Archer came to his senses underwater but couldn't tell which direction was up. Panicking, he blew air from his mouth, attempting to decipher which direction the bubbles floated. Bubbles scattered and he could not tell. A feeling of doom swept over him. He tried again but gained no vital information. Hypoxia was rapidly overtaking Archer's system. His muscles relaxed, and his body became limp. Archer's body bobbed with the gentle movements of the water. *Please...somebody... rescue me*, he prayed as he began to lose consciousness.

Archer awoke to complete silence and stillness. He felt the warmth of the sun on his skin as he laid on the sand. *Am I dead?* he thought. He pinched himself and felt the pain. His clothes were soaking wet. All indications pointed to him still being alive. He sat up, looked at his surroundings, and immediately recognized a familiar face. "Grandpa?" Archer asked.

"Hello, Archer," Franklin replied lovingly.

Archer began to weep happy tears as he got up to hug his grandfather. Suddenly his tears of joy turned to tears of sorrow. He became inconsolable.

"What's wrong, Archer?" Franklin asked.

"I'm dead, aren't I? This is all just an illusion inside of my head," Archer said between bouts of crying. "How else could I be talking to you?"

Franklin hugged his grandson tighter. "It all depends on how you approach the word *dead*."

"What do you mean, Grandpa?"

Franklin let go of Archer. "Let's get you dried off," he said. "We can discuss this further in a more comfortable place." Franklin put his hand on Archer's back and ushered him away from the beach.

Archer noticed that his grandfather was healthy and spry, like that of a man in his midtwenties. He also noticed that his grandfather was wearing a dazzling white suit that almost hurt his eyes to look at. Archer looked down and saw that he was wearing his embroidered black suit once again.

The two ascended a staircase that led them to a busy sidewalk. Archer realized he was once again in the Marketplace where he met Eric Muncie. "Look familiar?" Franklin asked.

"Too familiar," he replied. "How'd you know I've been here?"

"I watched you, of course. I'll be darned if I didn't see you run out of that basketball building like the dickens! You got your athleticism from me, you know?" he said as he elbowed Archer.

Archer laughed. "So I've heard. Why didn't I see you?"

"Because I concealed myself well enough from your sight. I was about to step inside when you didn't leave the building after a couple of years, though."

"A couple of years? You're wrong, Grandpa. I was there for, at most, a half hour."

Franklin smiled and said, "Maybe to you. But here, a half hour is like a couple of years, and a couple of years is like a half hour."

Archer was more confused.

"Ahh, here we are," Franklin said as they arrived at a small park a fair distance away from the buildings. "Sit. Take as much time as you need," Franklin said as they sat at a picnic table, enjoying the scenery. "No need to rush."

Archer took a moment to calm down from his near-death experience. Eventually the joy of being with his grandfather overtook his thoughts. "It's so great to see you, Grandpa," Archer finally said. "Life has been so difficult since you left. You were the only constant I could count on."

"I know. I miss you too," Franklin replied. "You're a strong boy, though. I know you've done very well for yourself since I passed on."

"Maybe," Archer replied, "But it sure would be easier if I had you there with me."

"Watching a loved one pass on is never an easy experience. That's for sure. Now let's get to it," Franklin said. "What questions do you have for me while we're here together?"

"Uhh...well," Archer replied, "what is this place? Seems like an appropriate place to start."

"Very good," Franklin said. He cleared his throat and began, "Archer, you are in the Transcendent realm. This realm is more real than any real life you currently know."

"Like a dream?" Archer asked.

Franklin shook his head and said, "Not in the slightest. What you're experiencing is more than a dream. It is a vision. Archer, you've been chosen from the very beginning to be able to see things wise men and women have requested to experience for millennia."

"So what you're saying is that all of this is real?"

"Yes."

"And this Transcendent realm is more real than my normal life."

"Yes. We call that the 'Earthly realm,'" Franklin said.

"Explain to me how this is all happening at the same time as my earthly life then," Archer asked.

61

"A better way to think about it is that the Transcendent realm is happening at every time and no time, all at the same time."

"Okay, you really lost me there," Archer said while scratching his head.

Franklin chuckled. "Don't worry too much about this fact. You can't be expected to understand this reality until you've transformed."

"Transformed?"

"Yes."

"And what do I become?" Archer asked.

"Well, who are you now?"

"I'm Archer Coleman. Seventeen-year-old human male," Archer said matter-of-factly.

"Is that it?" Franklin asked.

Archer thought about it. "Uhh…yeah? What else could I be?"

"Think about this Transcendent realm, Archer. How are you here right now? Did your physical seventeen-year-old body get here? Or did some other part of you transport here?"

Archer replied, "What kind of question is that? I'm a body. That's all I am. I'm a brain, and I'm a conscious sense of myself."

Franklin nodded and said, "That is where you are so fatally incorrect. A transcendent being is necessary to interact with the Transcendent realm."

"There's more to me than my earthly body? That can't be," Archer said.

"But it is so," Franklin replied. "This is one of the hardest lessons for humans to learn. I understand why it is so difficult for you to come to grips with this fact, but truth be told, you're very blessed to have the ability to see the Transcendent realm with your transcendent self. Most people are forced to believe this without seeing. You were chosen."

Archer replied, "And who do I have to thank for choosing me?"

Franklin bowed as he replied, "The King."

"The King?" Franklin bowed.

"Yes."

"So the Transcendent realm is actually a kingdom, and the ruler of the whole joint chose little ole me, Archer Coleman, to check it out for myself."

"Now you're getting it!" Franklin answered.

"I'm not buying it," Archer said.

"Come," Franklin said, saddened. "Let me show you something."

The two got up from the picnic table and walked back toward the busy streets of the Marketplace.

"Wait," Archer said, "before we go, I want to say thank you for saving me from drowning and bringing me to the beach."

"I appreciate your gratitude, but you're thanking the wrong person," Franklin replied.

"Who saved me then?"

Franklin bowed.

The two came to a halt in the Marketplace at a spot where they could watch the multitude of people passing by. "What do you see, Archer?" Franklin asked.

Archer took in all the happenings around him transpiring at a frenetic pace. "I see a million people walking superfast."

"And what do you notice about the people?"

Archer looked more intently at the crowd. "Well, I notice that they're all wearing suits like ours. Some are black and some are white."

Franklin clapped his hands together. "Fantastic! Now bring your attention to any individual that catches your eye. *Really* look at this person."

Archer looked into the crowd and locked on to a portly gentleman in his midforties, wearing a black suit. At first he looked unassuming and mild-mannered enough. However, the longer he looked at him, something strange happened. A contraption made of old wood appeared around the man's neck. "Woah. What is that?" Archer asked.

"That, Archer, is a yoke similar to ones that farmers of old placed around their team of beasts."

Archer listened intently.

"Everyone has a yoke, Archer. No one is exempt. The Earthly and the Transcendent realms are connected in this manner. The outward showing of the Transcendent realm merely reflects the internal of the human in the Earthly. In other words, that which dominates their earthly life also rules their inner being. People choose, actively or passively, what rules their transcendent, most real self.

"Now look deeper at the man," Franklin said.

Archer did so, and the yoke the man was wearing appeared to get heavier and more burdensome. The man looked as if his legs were going to give out from the weight on his shoulders. Suddenly, Archer saw a dollar sign appear above the man's head. The man's countenance began to fall with each second. The dollar sign appeared to be taking energy from the man as he looked more and more unhealthy.

"What do you see, Archer?" Franklin asked.

"Well, at first," Archer said, "the man looked all right, but the more I looked at him, the worse off he seems. I feel really bad for him."

Franklin replied, "The longer you look at them, the deeper you can look into their transcendent self. We call that one's soul."

Archer had never heard that word before.

"At first glance, most people look fine," Franklin explained. "However, those that aren't wearing the royal yoke look unhappier and unhappier as you gaze inwardly," Franklin said.

"Royal yoke? Like from that King you mentioned?" Archer asked.

Franklin bowed. "Precisely," Franklin said. "Now place your focus on someone wearing a white suit."

Archer turned his attention to the crowd and saw a golden yoke appear around the neck of a woman wearing a similar white suit as Franklin's.

"Now what do you see, Archer?"

"The royal yoke on the woman looks really heavy and restricting at first glance," Archer explained, "but once I really looked at her, it got lighter, and she began to have a glow about her." Archer kept his attention focused on her, and there appeared a crown above her head. Energy from the crown flowed toward the woman. "Wow," Archer said.

Franklin put his arm around Archer. "Just beautiful, isn't it?"

"It's incredible," Archer replied.

"Are you observing how others are treating this woman?"

"No," Archer replied.

"I suggest you do," Franklin said.

Archer followed the woman as she walked down the sidewalk.

"Get out of here, scum!" Archer heard a worker from one of the buildings shout.

"You're ruining our business!" yelled another.

"It sounds like they hate her," Archer noted.

"Indeed," Franklin replied. "And how is she responding?"

Archer watched the woman simply walk past and wave at the people hurling insults at her.

"Despite the insults," Franklin said, "she has transformed into someone capable of showing love and compassion to these people who wish ill upon her. And she *genuinely* means it."

Archer was taken aback. "Why would she do that?" Archer asked. "Shouldn't she stand up for herself?"

"She lets His Highness stand up for her now," Franklin replied. "Now," Franklin said, "take a good, long look at me."

Archer did so, and the same transformation occurred to his grandfather. A golden yoke appeared around his neck and a crown shone above his head. "How do you do that?" Archer asked.

"Ahh, that's the key," Franklin replied. "I did not do anything, and neither did she. No human has the ability to transform themselves into such beings."

"But I saw it with her and with you. Is it some kind of optical illusion?" Archer asked.

"Of course not!" Franklin replied. "Your vision is perfect. His Highness did this for us long ago. By donning His yoke, we become like Him."

"What did He do for us? How does it work?" Archer asked.

Franklin smiled. "All great questions that we will work through together. But first, Arch, we must deal with you. Have you yet thought about what your yoke looks like?"

Archer looked at his reflection in the window of a building. "But I'm not wearing one, Grandpa. I don't feel anything around me."

"But you are, Archer," Franklin said. "Everyone wears one, remember? And you, whether you like it or not, fall into the category of everyone."

Archer looked again at his reflection. "Why don't I see one then?"

"Because you've never taken the time to think about what you've surrendered your life to," Franklin explained. "In fact, most people never think about it. They never see the yoke around their necks."

"Okay, sure. Maybe I haven't. But I want to now! How do I do it?" Archer asked.

"I will show you," Franklin replied. "Close your eyes," Franklin instructed Archer. "Good. Now I want you to think about your life. Don't just think about the superficialities of it. Really dig deep. Ask yourself questions like what makes you most happy? What would you most get up out of bed for at 4:00 a.m. and do for free? What do you love watching or listening to most? Think about these questions, and you'll begin to see it."

Archer stood with his eyes shut, while onlookers gave him strange looks.

"Stop harassing the boy!" a man in a black suit shouted at Franklin.

"Shh," Franklin said, "he's concentrating."

The man was swept away with the crowd before he could stop and respond.

"This is hard," Archer said after a while. "I don't feel like I've ever been consumed by anything to that kind of level."

"Surely something came to your mind," Franklin replied.

"I mean, not really," Archer said. "But if I had to say one thing, I think it would have to be my parents and siblings. I'd say they're probably the most meaningful objects in my life." Archer thought for another moment. "Although," he said, "my HQ score might be a close second."

"Very good," Franklin said. "Now look at your reflection once more."

Archer turned his attention to the window. He watched as a wooden yoke appeared around his neck. He started to notice just how much weight was pressing down on him. His reflection began to appear ill and weak. He looked up above his head and saw what looked like a picture frame. "Grandpa, I think I see it now," Archer said. "What's above my head?"

"It's a picture of you as a young boy with your parents, Adrian, Jamie, and myself."

"What does it mean?" Archer asked.

"What lies above our yoke is what we are surrendered to," Franklin answered. "And yours is an interesting item."

"What makes it interesting?" Archer asked.

"There are an infinite number of things in our lives in which we can surrender our earthly life and, consequently, our soul to. Humans are more attuned to the disastrous effects some objects create as compared to others, such as addiction to money, brutality, and power. Others have a more benign appearance. Family is one such object."

"But how could loving my family ever be considered a bad thing?" Archer asked.

"Loving your family is not in itself an undesirable trait," Franklin replied. "It becomes dangerous only when we place anything other than His Highness on the throne of our heart. It is like placing a human in outer space with no spacesuit. Earthly matters were not created to function properly in the Transcendent."

Archer continued to look at his reflection. The family portrait was draining energy from his unhealthy, damaged self. "For the record, I still think all this yoke and suit and crown business is all phooey, and there's gotta be a good explanation."

Franklin smiled and said, "I sense a 'but' statement is going to be uttered."

Archer chuckled. "Yes, I don't believe this is real," Archer said. "Buuuuuttttttt, say a guy wanted to switch his old, wooden yoke for a golden one. How does totally-not-me, Mr. Hypothetical Guy, go about doing that?"

"Well, you'd have to get it from the King." Franklin bowed. "Do you wish to see Him?"

"The King?" Archer exclaimed.

Franklin bowed.

"Why would he want to talk to us? He's got to be busy being a King and all, right?"

"His Highness always makes time for each and every one of His subjects," Franklin replied.

"Let's do it!" Archer exclaimed. "Let's get this ugly thing off of me!"

"Very well," Franklin said. "His residence is this way. If you are ever lost and want to find Him again, just head north."

Together they enter into the busy stream of people and begin to walk in the opposite direction of the flow of the crowd. Archer watched as a young boy he figured to be around fourteen or fifteen years old was led into a building with bright flashing letters and dancers in the windows. The sign read PORNOGRAPHY." His heart felt an intense sadness for the boy. He stopped Franklin and asked, "Does each building have the ability to place your first yoke on you?"

"No," Franklin replied. "Everyone is born with a yoke, and we are unable to escape this reality. The ones in the building are only able to place themselves as the person's master. If you remember, the picture above your head was placed there by workers in the 'FAMILY' building."

"No, they didn't," Archer said. "I don't remember that at all."

"Don't feel bad, Archer," Franklin replied. "Most people do not remember the exact moment this occurs."

Archer looked at the PORNOGRAPHY building again. "Will that happen to that boy, Grandpa?" he asked. "Are they going to become his master?"

"It's not a guarantee," Franklin replied. "Just think back to your experience in the BASKETBALL building. You were able to escape its clutches."

"Is there any way we can help?" Archer asked.

"What we can do now is pray for this boy and what he is going through," Franklin answered.

"Pray?" Archer asked.

"Yes, pray. We can ask His Majesty to provide help to this boy so he may be able to escape as unscathed as possible, if it be in His will. It is the best tool we have to fight for this boy."

"What good is that gonna do? He can't even hear us," Archer said.

"But He can. He is with us always, whether we know it or not."

"That's creepy," Archer said.

Franklin shook his head. "Not in the slightest, Archer. It is an immensely comforting feeling when properly recognized."

Just then, the two watched as the boy was escorted out of the building by one of its salespeople. "We cannot wait to help you solve all the problems you are facing, young man. You will not regret working under us. Come back anytime!"

"Thanks!" the boy exclaimed. The boy entered the stream of people on the sidewalk and disappeared from their sight.

Franklin sighed a heavy sigh. "That young man is in for the fight of his life, Archer. Theirs is one of the most difficult contracts to get out of. The increasing popularity of their contract is a most unsettling fact about the Earthly realm."

Archer wanted nothing more in that moment than for that boy to rip up the contract he had just signed and be free.

"Chin up, Archer. Let's keep going."

Archer struggled to walk against the heavy flow of traffic in the heart of the Marketplace. However, the crowd thinned out the farther north they traversed, and he was able to walk more freely. The sidewalk became thinner and thinner until Archer and Franklin were forced one in front of the other. The flashing lights and commotion of the downtown Marketplace had since subsided. Archer could hear birds chirping and started to feel too warm in his suit jacket.

"We are almost there, Archer." Franklin said. "Start to think about the questions you would like to ask His Majesty, and He will be more than happy to answer them for you."

Archer's heart began to race at the idea of meeting this person. Suddenly Archer became worried about what the King might think of his big, ugly yoke. Shame and guilt flooded Archer's body. "I can't do it," Archer told Franklin.

"You can't do what?" Franklin asked.

Archer began to walk the other way. "I can't see the King."

Franklin bowed. "And why not?"

"For one, its seems like I'm not dressed appropriately," he said as he tugged at his black suit. "And two, I know nothing about the guy. From what you're saying, I chose my family over Him. He's obviously not gonna be happy about that! I wouldn't be happy about that if it was me. I think it's best if I just turn around and head home. Maybe I'll see Him next time. Yeah! Let's plan on that. Next time." Archer turned around and began to head south.

"What if there is no next time?" Franklin asked somberly.

Archer stopped in his tracks. He paused and mulled over this question. "I don't know, Grandpa," he finally responded.

"What if there is no next time?" Franklin walked back and put his hand on Archer's shoulder. "Let's not think about that possibility at this moment. Just come. Trust me, Archer. His Majesty desires nothing more than to see you."

Something inside Archer wanted this to be true. "Okay," Archer said. "I'll go with you."

Archer turned around and followed his grandfather's footsteps once more. As they approached the end of the sidewalk, the light in front of them became brighter and brighter. Archer had to shield his eyes as he could no longer handle the intensity. He was forced into holding on to his grandfather's hand to help guide him forward. Archer could barely make out that they were headed toward a gate. They approached the gate, and the warmth and intensity of the light was causing Archer to sweat profusely in his black suit. Singing could also be heard in the distance. "Their voices are so beautiful!" Archer shouted.

The heat and the singing and the light continued to intensify with each laborious step forward. The stimuli of the environment pierced his soul. Archer ripped off his jacket and pants from the heat. He could no longer stand to open his eyes, and he crouched down covering his ears with his hands to shield himself from the noise. He began to sob from the feeling of insignificance that consumed him.

"Archerrrr!" he heard faintly. "Archerrrr!" He dared not open his eyes. "Archer! Get up!" he heard.

"LEAVE ME ALONE!" he shouted. "I DIDN'T ASK FOR THIS!"

"Archer, you have to get up. You're going to be late!"

"I can't! I can't! I can't!" he shouted repeatedly. Archer continued to weep in the crouched position.

After a few moments had passed, Archer brought his crying down to a manageable level. He began to wonder where his grandfather had gone as he no longer heard Franklin's voice. Cautiously he released pressure from his right ear and only heard silence. He slowly opened one eye and saw that he was back in his bedroom.

"Archer! You have to get up and get ready for school or you're going to be late!" Henry shouted from outside of his door. "I'm not going to tell you again!"

Archer looked at the clock beside his bed and saw it was 7:43 in the morning. "Okay, okay, I'm up!" Archer shouted back. "I'll get ready! Geez!" Archer rushed around his room to get ready for the day and sped off to school without another thought of what had transpired that night.

CHAPTER 6

Off to College

Archer woke up to the sound of his alarm clock but, unlike most days, he did not hit the snooze button. Archer immediately popped out of bed, showered, and proudly donned his Helmuth University T-shirt. The final day of Archer's senior year had arrived. Seniors at Morrison High School wear the T-shirt or sweatshirt of the university they plan to attend the following fall semester. Archer felt a great sense of excitement as he drove to Morrison High School one final time.

"We did it, brother!" Archer said to Ty in the parking lot as they did their handshake.

"Feels just like yesterday we were two snot-nosed kindergarten kids playing together on the playground," Ty said.

"Isn't it crazy? And now look at us. Adults. All grown up," said seventeen-year-old Archer. "You know, Ty, I still think you should have applied to a better school than the community college here in town. You're way smarter than any of the other kids going there. And there's no way your HQ score improved much. I didn't even see you post about it?"

Ty looked away and then back up at Archer. "Well, Arch, the thing is, I think we both want different things out of life," Ty said. "I'm the first one in my family to go to college, and I'm really proud of that, no matter where I go. Plus I know what I want to do, and they have a really good—"

"Oh…no…I wasn't trying to be mean, Ty," Archer said, "Honest, I just was saying—"

Ty interrupted, "It's all good, man. I know you didn't mean anything by it. I just mean you've gotten so wrapped up with your HQ score this year. I'm a little worried that you chose Helmuth only for the points and that you might be setting yourself up for unhappiness down the road. Our scores are important and all, but should we base all our choices on it?"

Archer put his hand on Ty's shoulder. "Look, I appreciate your concern. That's what friends are for, right?" Archer asked. "Okay, yeah, I admit that I did enjoy the *hefty* score bump I got." Archer emphasized *hefty*, much to Ty's chagrin. "And honestly, yeah, I kinda do think we should base our biggest life choices on it. That's what it was designed to do. But that's beside the point. That's not the only reason I'm going there. I genuinely want to get a job that helps people get more out of life, and that degree will allow me to do that."

Ty wasn't buying it, but he was supportive of his friend. "All right, man. I believe you. Just don't forget to stay in touch after you make all your fancy college friends."

"Don't you worry for a second, chief," Archer said. "I'll remember all you little people when I make it to the top."

The two boys walked into school to the sight of green and orange balloons lining the halls. Archer puffed his chest out slightly more than usual to make sure his T-shirt was legible to everyone within eyeshot. "Wow, Helmuth!" he heard someone exclaim.

Archer could practically sense his HQ score rising by the second. "Ty, look at that!"

"What?" he asked.

"It's Grace," Archer said, directing Ty's attention in her direction. "THE Grace. You know, that one girl named Grace in our class. About five-foot-eight, pretty eyes. That Grace."

Ty laughed. "Yes, Archer, I've known her as long as you. Spit it out. What about her?"

Archer stood frozen in the hallway, speechless.

"What are you doing?" Ty asked. "Did she just levitate or something?"

"Even better," Archer replied, frozen with his mouth agape.

Ty grabbed his friend by the shoulders and shook him, "Out with it, man! Speak to me!"

"Look," Archer said.

Ty looked at Grace as she stood talking to friends. He looked back at Archer. "What's so special about her today?"

"Her shirt," Archer whispered as he could barely get the words out.

"Her what?" Ty asked.

"Her shirt," Archer said even more quietly.

"Come on man, quit playing!" Ty said. "Say it!"

Archer looked Ty square in the eyes. "Her shirt! Her shirt! Don't you get it? Her shirt says Helmuth University."

Ty immediately let go of his grip on Archer. "Are you serious?" Ty asked. "You sure you're not just seeing what you want to see?" Sure enough, Ty recognized the Helmuth University logo on the sweatshirt that Grace was wearing. "Dude, you're right!" Ty exclaimed. "You gotta go talk to her!"

"I...I...I...," Archer stammered. "I think I do." Archer collected himself mentally and walked over coolly to Grace. He waited for the right time in the conversation with her friends to interrupt. He felt a small lull in the conversation and butted in. "Grace!" he said as he pointed back and forth from his shirt toward hers. "Why didn't you tell me you were going to Helmuth!"

Grace separated herself from the group. "Archer! You know? I really just wanted to see the look on your face when you found out. Surprise!"

The two hugged.

"This is amazing!" Archer said. "When did you get accepted?"

"I got accepted early, maybe around September."

Archer narrowed his eyes. "So you're telling me you knew this whole time and didn't say anything. You're a jerk!"

Grace laughed. "I guess I am, but the look on your face right now was totally worth it," she said.

Just then, a buzz went off in the school, and the usual announcement that followed announced, "ONE MINUTE UNTIL CLASS. I REPEAT. ONE MINUTE UNTIL CLASS."

Archer and Grace began walking to class. "Well, Archer, we definitely should get together and talk more about it before we move in to Helmuth," Grace said.

Archer agreed. "I'd really like that."

The two walked in the classroom and sat at their respective seats.

"Congratulations, class!" said Mr. Locke. "Today is the big day! I'm always so surprised by how quickly each school year flies by. Surprised and saddened," he said as he mimicked a tear falling down his face. "Alas, that's the reality in which we teachers find ourselves. You start to make connections with the kids and *BOOM*! They're off to who-knows-where doing who-knows-what leaving ole Mr. Locke here in this classroom, all by himself. All alone. Cold. Scared. It's not fair!" he said, faking a child's temper tantrum.

The class chuckled at his silliness. "But then, at the nadir of my sorrow, I see a light emerging from the darkness. Hello! Who is it? Just take my wallet, I don't want any trouble!" he said as he crouched down and tossed his wallet away from him.

Archer caught it.

"It's another class of students come to save me from my despair! Oh may your HQ scores rise like the fiery sun in the sky! Praise be to you, children!" he exclaimed with hands raised to the ceiling.

The class clapped as Mr. Locke took a bow for his performance.

"Thank you! Thank you! I've been working on that routine for, let's see," he looked at his watch, "Oh, about twenty-two years now. I'm still waiting on my invitation to the Tony's, but I haven't lost hope! This thespian will never give up hope!" he said with one arm raised upward in front of him.

Archer smiled and wished that today was not his last day in Mr. Locke's class.

"My goal today," the teacher continued as he grabbed his wallet from Archer, "is to impart some final words of wisdom on you young scholars. If you don't remember *anything* that we learned from this year, first off, you'll make me a sad, old man. But if that's the case, I'll get over it once you begin to think about the big picture of the HQ. Please respect the system in place. Honor it. Heroes from our past nobly fought the good fight to get us where we are. Our nation was on the brink of rotting from the inside out. Old ways of thinking needed to be replaced for our society to move ahead socially, economically, and politically. Racism, sexism, all of the other -isms, defeated in one fell swoop," he said, swinging his imaginary ax. "Scientific discoveries are now allowed to progress untrammeled by archaic ways of thinking. We are truly one step closer to the Day!" Mr. Locke said.

"And it can't come soon enough!" the class shouted.

"Haha! I love it!" he exclaimed, clasping his hands together. "It's been such a pleasure teaching you all this year, and I sincerely wish you all the best in your individual paths to happiness," Mr. Locke said with a bow.

Students lined up to shake Mr. Locke's hand as some brought him small gifts as a token of their appreciation.

The school buzz went off, and the doors slid open. The students packed up their backpacks and began exiting the room. "Oh, Archer," Mr. Locke said through the commotion, "could you stay behind and chat for a second?"

"Sure!" Archer said excitedly.

They waited for the room to clear.

"Archer, I am so proud of the student you were this year. Your mother and I spoke at the start of the year about our goals for you. You hit every single one of them."

"Thank you, Mr. Locke," Archer said. "That means a lot coming from you."

"You're very welcome," he replied. "Can I tell you something else?" he asked.

Archer nodded his head up and down. He was hanging on every word of his beloved teacher.

"Archer, you were the only student in the class to get a perfect score on the final exam. You're one of the few students I've taught that have accomplished this feat. It's no surprise you'll be attending such a prestigious institution like Helmuth next fall. And in the social engineering department, no less! My heart swells with pride knowing that I will have played a small part in the eventual success you will achieve in the future. Who knows? Maybe you'll be running the Department of Wealth one day. I know you have it in you!" he said.

"Thank you," Archer replied. "You're too kind."

"It's the HQ-honest truth," Mr. Locke said. "Now go enjoy your last day."

Archer firmly shook Mr. Locke's hand and left the classroom.

The rest of the day passed in a blur, as did the graduation ceremony that followed on Saturday. Archer had always dreamed of the day when he would complete high school. He couldn't wait to leave town and go to college. However, he didn't anticipate the conflicting feelings that would accompany graduation day. Thinking about never seeing people he spent so much time with throughout the years was an uncomfortable thought for him. Archer also felt bitter that he was leaving after finally finding his true self and niche within his class community. However, the sweet feeling of leaving town and going to college outweighed all those sentiments. He couldn't wait to begin attaining a collegiate-level understanding of the HQ system and philosophy as a whole.

Archer spent most of his summer working his normal summer job and hanging out with his friends. He began preparing for his move to Helmuth around two days before the big move. "Mom!" he shouted one morning from his upstairs bedroom.

"What?" Nicole shouted back from the kitchen.

"How many pairs of socks do you think I'll need to bring?" Archer asked. "What about boxers? Oh no! What if I don't have enough boxers!" he shouted while buzzing around his bedroom.

Nicole walked upstairs to help calm him down. "Archer, whatever you bring is going to be okay. They have stores on campus, you know?"

"Oh, yeah," he said. "I guess you're right. Thanks. I'm just so nervous and excited and happy and sad and, and, and nervous, all at the same time. It's hard for me to think straight."

Nicole tried comforting her son. "I remember feeling the same way before I moved out for college. But you know what?"

"What?" Archer asked.

"Those feelings began to disappear the moment I stepped onto campus and spent that first night in my dorm room. Of course some people get homesick, and that's natural, but I have a feeling you'll do just fine."

"I think so too," Archer added.

"I always knew you would go off and do big things in life," Nicole added. "You've got a date with destiny, Archer."

The two hugged.

"Speaking of dates," Nicole said. "When are you going to ask that cute friend of yours, Grace, out on a date? I saw she's going to Helmuth too!"

Archer's face turned red. He realized at that moment that he had forgotten about her proposal to meet up during the summer. "Ha! Oh, her?" he asked, "Nah, we're just good friends, that's all. She, uh, she's, uh, not my type. Yeah! She's not exactly my type, so we'll just keep that one on the back burner, if you know what I mean. If it happens, it happens, you know?"

"Oh yes, sureeeee," Nicole said. "Back burner. Got it. I understand now. Well that's a relief because I heard a rumor floating around school that you liked her and wanted to—"

"Okay! Okay!" Archer said as he ushered his mother out of the bedroom, "I think that's enough chitchat for one afternoon. I've got a lot of packing to do, and you know what they say! There's no time like the present!"

"All right, honey," Nicole said, "Just give me a shout if you have any other questions. You know, like how many books do you bring? How many scarves? How to ask a nice girl from your hometown that coincidentally goes to the same college as you out to a nice date at a restaurant? You know, the basics of college?"

"Yeah, yeah, sure, sure, the girl. I'll keep that in mind. Okay, out you go!" he said as he shut the door.

Two days later, Archer finished packing his car and was on the road to Helmuth University. Archer, Henry, and Nicole all cried as he pulled out of the driveway and began the eight-hour drive to campus. Once the tears dried up, and the sadness subsided, Archer felt a sense of freedom like he had never known before. "I'm actually doing it," he said aloud. "Helmuth, here I come, baby!"

Archer could not contain his joy upon arrival. He drove through the heart of campus and looked on with wild imagination at all the great buildings. He wondered how many great discussions and brilliant ideas had been conjured up inside of them. *Some of the most legendary people to shape our society have been exactly where I am right now*, he thought to himself. He parked his car outside the dorm hall, got out, and confidently proclaimed, "I'm home."

Moving his things into his dorm room was quite simple as he was never one to have a lot of things. He finished making his bed, laid there for a moment, and began to daydream about the first day of classes the following morning. Just then, Archer heard a knock on the door. Archer's roommate had not yet arrived, so he got up quickly to let in whomever was at the door.

"Grandpa?" Archer stuck his head out of the door, looked left and looked right, but did not see anyone else in the halls. "Does anyone else see you?"

"Archer, we don't have a lot of time," Franklin said. "Please, let me in."

"Come in, come in," Archer said.

Franklin sat on the empty bed opposite Archer's. "Please listen very carefully, Archer," Franklin said, seriously. "You are in grave danger."

Archer, sitting on his bed, looked at his deceased grandfather with understandable confusion. He pinched himself and felt the pain.

"Archer! I'm serious! I don't have a lot of time. I've been given strict orders to make this trip short and sweet."

"Okay, Grandpa," he said. "I'm listening." Archer had never seen his grandfather with such a concerned look on his face.

"Archer, there is a battle being waged for your soul. There always has been, don't get me wrong, but the stakes have *greatly* increased."

"What raised the stakes so greatly?" Archer asked.

"I don't have the time to explain but, please, please, Archer, think about His Highness and His goodness while you're here. Antipalos seeks your destruction." Franklin looked all around the room nervously. "Okay, I have to go now," he said. "I can't be here another second. Goodbye, Archer." Franklin rushed out of the room and slammed it shut.

"Wait!" Archer asked, chasing after his grandfather. "What battle? Who's Antipalos? Why does this keep happening to me?"

Archer ran to the door and flung it open to catch a glimpse of his grandfather. Instead, there stood a slender, dark-haired boy with a raised fist about to knock on the door.

"Woah. How'd you know I was here?" he asked Archer.

Archer cleared his throat. "Well, I, uh, heard someone outside of the door and thought, you know, I'd better let them in just in case their hands were full!"

His roommate smiled, "Thanks, man! I think I'm gonna like you!" Archer's roommate placed some things on the floor next to his bed. "Howdy, my name's Knox. What's yours?" he said, extending his hand out toward Archer.

"Archer. Archer Coleman. It's great to meet you, Knox."

"The pleasure's all mine," Knox said. "Say, Archer, you know where the bathrooms are?"

"Down the hall to the right, and they'll be at the very end," Archer answered. "If you fall down the stairs, you've gone too far."

"Hahaha! Oh man, you're funny too! I hit the roommate jackpot!" Knox said as he slapped Archer on the back.

"I'll be right back," he said.

"Sounds good," Archer replied.

Archer sat on the bed in silence, contemplating the vision with his grandfather. He recalled what Franklin told him in the Transcendent realm: "What you're experiencing is more than a dream. It is a vision. Archer, you've been chosen from the very beginning to be able to see things wise men and women have requested for millennia to experience." This did make some sense to Archer as he had never heard anyone else speak of such an experience. And these visions felt like real life, not like normal dreams. "Could it all be *true*?" he asked aloud.

"Could what be true?" Knox asked as he entered the room again.

Archer's posture straightened up immediately. "Oh, nothing. Just, uh, thinking about how busy my schedule is gonna be for the semester and how little time I'll have to play basketball at the rec center. You know me! Gotta have my b-ball!"

Knox laughed. "Well, seein' as we just met five minutes ago," Knox said, "I don't really know ya quite yet, but hey, gotta do what you gotta do to stay sane, brother!"

Archer agreed. "That's right, man. What do you like to do in your free time?"

Knox continued to unpack his things. "Well, truth be told, lately I've become laser focused on increasing my HQ score. Researching the algorithm, reading blogs from experts at the top…you know, nerdy stuff. In fact, I used to think it was all a bunch of nonsense, but there's just something about seeing your name rise up that scoreboard that makes a person want to keep on climbin' to the summit!"

"Dude, I was the same exact way before senior year philosophy class," Archer said, excitedly. "It all changed after that. It's honestly an addiction."

"Indeed, but a healthy addiction," Knox said scholarly.

"Indubitably," Archer replied. Archer knew at that moment the two of them would become great friends.

The next day, Archer woke up and walked to the dining hall for breakfast with Knox. "So Knox, what's your major?" he asked.

"I'm undecided right now, actually. But I'm leanin' toward economics. My dad's an economist for the Department of Worth, and I could see myself working in that space. It's funny, though. I always said I would never end up doing what my old man does, but here we are. Eight-year-old Knox would kick my butt if he heard me sayin' all this to you!"

"Man, I'm in the same boat," Archer replied. "My dad works for the DOW as an HQ engineer, and I never really knew a lot about what he did until a couple of years ago. It seemed like something I could see myself doing once I learned more about it. Not the engineering side so much as the philosophical side of what the DOW does."

The two boys walked in the dining hall and began to fill their trays with breakfast foods. "What kind of job does a philosophy degree get you?" Knox asked.

"Well, according to my research online," Archer replied, "philosophy majors are in high demand at the DOW. They're constantly reading data and passing that information along to engineers so they can tweak the algorithms and make HQ scores as accurate as possible."

The boys sat down at a table and began eating. "That's pretty cool, man. Good luck to ya," Knox said with a mouth full of yogurt.

"I appreciate it. You, too, Knox." Archer looked at his watch and realized class began in five minutes. "Oh no!" he shouted. "I gotta get going. I'll see you tonight, Knox!"

"See ya, buddy! Have fun!"

Archer whipped his backpack on one shoulder and zipped out of the dining hall, speed walking away from the cafeteria. "Okay, let's see. Which class do I have first?" Archer asked himself as he opened a picture of his schedule on his phone. Philosophy 111. 9:00 a.m. Chernyshevsky Hall. *Where the heck is Chernyshevsky Hall? Aww man, I'm gonna be late on the first day! I can't make a bad first impression. What if it's a small class? Everyone will see me! Oh no!* he said in his head as he furiously searched for a campus map online.

Archer felt a tap on the shoulder. He looked up and saw a friendly-looking older gentleman. "Can I help you?" Archer asked him.

"You look lost, son. First day?" he asked.

"Look, I've gotta get to Chernyshevsky Hall in two minutes before class starts. Do you know the quickest way?"

"Of course I do!" he said. "Here, let me show you the way." The older gentleman grabbed Archer by the shoulders and turned him around.

Archer read the engraving above the front entrance that read "Chernyshevsky Hall." "Ahh…right," Archer said. "Thank you."

The gentleman nodded. "No thanks necessary. Good luck on your first day, Archer!"

Archer rushed inside the building and found his room. He opened the door to a giant lecture hall filled with what appeared to be at least two hundred students. Archer had never been in a class with more than twenty-five other students. He found a seat near the back and got out his notebook and a pen.

"Good morning, young scholars!" the professor's voice belted over the speakers. "My name is Dr. Marco Espinoza. I'll be your lecture professor for Philosophy 111: Intro to Philosophy."

Archer furiously scribbled this information in his notebook.

"Philosophy is a required course for every student here at Helmuth University, but this course is specifically tailored for philosophy majors. Therefore, we will be taking a deeper dive into the fascinating world of philosophy and its application to today's society as compared to students of other majors who get more of a thirty-thousand-foot overview. Pity for them," he said as he paced on stage. "Armed with this knowledge, YOU students are the world changers of tomorrow. YOU will work in prominent places to preserve this great democracy. YOU will define what success means in our society. YOU will become tomorrow's Freedom Fighters."

Euphoria filled Archer's soul. He underlined what he had written: *I will be tomorrow's Freedom Fighter.*

Dr. Espinoza continued, "Now, as I understand it, every American student has taken a basic course of this subject in high school. In this course, we will be briefly reviewing some of the same material, simply as a refresher. I will be plowing the field, pre-planting to prepare a nice, even seedbed, so to speak. After that, we will begin to ask life's most difficult questions and work through their answers. We'll discuss: What does a successful life entail? What is truth? What was religion? And most importantly, how does that impact our lives today?"

Archer hung on every word that came out of Dr. Espinoza's mouth. These were the questions he had always wanted answered but never knew how to ask them.

Once Philosophy 111 finished, Archer fulfilled the rest of his duties for the day. He and Knox agreed to meet at the dining hall for dinner together to recap their first days. "So how'd it go, Arch?

Everything you've ever hoped and dreamed of?" Knox asked as they sat down with trays full of food.

"That and more," Archer said. "How about you?"

"Great," he replied. "I mean I'm not lookin' forward to all that math in my econ classes, but I think it'll be fun." Knox took a big bite of his taco and continued, "Man, you shoulda heard one of my professors pumping us up. 'You will be tomorrow's leaders! You will transform the world!' All that jazz. Pretty inspiring to think about, considering so many people have left here and done some amazing things."

Archer agreed. "My first professor gave us the same spiel this morning. Definitely makes for a good tactic to get me to come to class every day!"

"You're not kiddin'!" Knox replied.

The boys finished their dinner and went to their dorm room. After settling in, the two of them decided to go to sleep in preparation for the next day's classes. "Good night, Knox," Archer said from his side of the room.

"Good night, buddy," he replied. "Don't let the bedbugs bite."

CHAPTER 7

Hamster Wheels

"Quiet down, class! We've got a lot of ground to cover today," Professor Espinoza said sternly. "Today marks the halfway point of the semester, so I want to be the first to congratulation each and every one of you on completing one-fourth of one-fourth of a bachelor's degree. Give it up for yourselves!"

The class roared with applause.

"Yes! That's the kind of energy I love this early in the morning!" he shouted. Dr. Espinoza took a sip of coffee while the class settled itself down.

"Thus far, we have superficially discussed religion and its deleterious effects on societies of yore. But what *really* was religion? Why did humans invent such nonsense? Well, believe it or not, religion did play a role in the development of human societies. Religion was what citizens created to escape the unanswered questions of life, the not-so-nice aspects of life. Why are we here? What's my purpose? Why is there pain? These types of questions—questions of morality and ethics."

Archer was enthralled.

"Religion was how humans kept ourselves sane," he explained. "Although outdated, religion used to serve a purpose. However, the minor benefits manifested by religious thinking are mightily outweighed by its consequences. You see, religion creates 'other' groups and teaches its followers to despise the 'others.' This is without fail. Yes, throughout our history, *religion,*" he said in a disgusted tone, "was the main cause of war, of famine, of torture, and of death." Professor Espinoza stopped for dramatic effect. "Therefore, reasoned the modern intellects, we could rid the world of all war and conflict toward one another, if we could rid the world of religion. What a brilliantly simple idea this turned out to be.

"Without religion, we would evolve as a human race, so went the argument. And is that what we observed once we divorced ourselves from such primitive thinking?" he asked the class facetiously. "Of course it is! Look around us! Nations that have adopted the HQ system have not warred against one another since its inception. We are truly one step closer to the Day!" Professor Espinoza said.

"And it can't come soon enough!" the class shouted.

"Ahh," he said, putting his hand over his chest, "it warms my heart to see the future of our nation in such good hands.

"Now this shift from religion to reason and science began well before the HQ system was implemented for good. A period known as the Enlightenment shed light, hence the name, on the atrocities of religion and truly brought human civilization out of the dark ages. We had outgrown religion like when a child lives long enough to outgrow the idea that their parents are superheroes. Postpubescent mankind's prefrontal cortex was now fully activated, and it kicked religion to the curb," he said with a kicking motion. "At this point, the only thing left to contend with was how to deal with the not-so-nice parts of life that religious answers once provided as anesthesia. *This* is the starting point for modern philosophical thought."

Archer continued to write frantically to keep pace with the eccentric professor.

Professor Espinoza continued, "Heroic thinkers of modern time discovered that what we call 'truth' is *subjective.* The discovery of truth's subjectivity was the proverbial nail in the cross to the divisive idea of universal truths."

Archer's head was spinning from all this new information.

"Universal moral and ethical truths," the professor continued, "simply do not exist. Let that truth sear into your brains. Anyone that tries to convince you otherwise is a con artist. And just what are they selling you? Hatred and bigotry. Plain and simple," he said with passion through clenched teeth.

"Without universal truths, any action is now permissible and truthful so long as the person's behavior does not hurt society or its members. What is true for one person may not be true for the next. Who's to judge what is right and wrong? After all, life does not have an instruction manual. Life's most difficult questions are not answered from some being far away in the sky, you see. They are answered from within," he said, beating his chest.

Many in the crowd began to beat their chests in a similar fashion.

"Now let's get to the heart of the issue," Dr. Espinoza said. "I will now explain to you *why* truth's subjectivity was such an important discovery."

"Why truth's sub is important" Archer wrote in his notebook.

"The importance of the discovery lies in the fact that people are now able to genuinely pursue what they define as 'happiness' without the religious barriers of hatred and bigotry that served as an insurmountable roadblock for our societies. People are individuals, first and foremost, and they are entitled to define what makes them happy or successful or valuable. We now vehemently believe that outside influences may not infringe upon this right, as was the case with religious thought. Individuals were once told what they must do or how they must act to be happy, successful, and valuable. Well, 'No more!' said the Freedom Fighters!" he shouted with a fist raised to the sky.

"The Freedom Fighters brilliantly devised a society that allowed both the unbridled pursuit of happiness and created a system that incentivized behavior that benefited society. I am speaking, of course, of the HQ system and the Law of Outer Perception. We now have a system in place that answers the question: 'How do I win at life?'"

Archer stopped his writing immediately. "How *do* I win at life?" he asked himself for the first time in his life.

The professor remained silent for a minute as his students pondered their answers. "Very few people, like celebrities and politicians, win at life," he explained. "Everyone else loses. And if that's the case, don't you think you should be striving to be one of the winners? Don't you think you should be on the right team headed in the right direction, pulling yourself and humanity upward? The HQ system is designed to do just that. It's designed to help us win by keeping us all on track. We get points for doing good, lose points for doing bad, and those with the most points win. It's as simple as that."

Archer felt increasingly like a loser the more he thought about his average HQ ranking. He had struggled with his self-confidence as a kid, so he was familiar with those thoughts. However, this time, the feelings of inferiority cut deeper. Being labeled a loser by someone as highly educated and respected as Professor Espinoza hurt tremendously. *It must be true if he's saying it*, Archer thought.

Professor Espinoza continued, "Therefore, young scholars, dedicate your lives to winning. Make every decision based on winning. I urge you to be the best in your field, to have the highest salary in your neighborhood, to gain the most recognition in your sphere of influence. All of these maximize serotonin and dopamine, the pleasure chemicals in your brain. Winning is about maximizing pleasure, minimizing pain, and not hindering anyone else's pursuit of happiness."

"Maximize happy, minimize pain, do not hinder others" Archer wrote in bullet point form.

"'Isn't that totally selfish? I thought we were supposed to help pull humanity upward?' you may be thinking. What a wise question!" he said with his index finger raised in the air. "Selfishness, when done properly, benefits everyone. True selfishness is selflessness. Becoming the most productive member of society you can be is good for everyone around you. Most importantly, there is merit in doing our part and advancing the human race, so that one day, there will be no more disease, no more war, no more suffering of any kind. This is the meaning of the Day that can't come soon enough. Each and every one of us is on a march toward humanity's perfection and, one day, we will find ourselves in this perfect society full of winners! What a glorious day that will be!"

Many in the crowd, including Archer, cheered.

Professor Espinoza drank in the applause. He continued, "People are inherently good, you see, and this goodness is allowed to shine in an HQ-based society. Our institutions of love and tolerance are harnessing humanity's goodness. Everyone is now free to do what they like, succeed at it, and get rewarded for it. As a result, the world will be a better place tomorrow and the next day and the next, until one day, we arrive at the finished product. We are truly one step closer to the Day!" Professor Espinoza shouted.

"AND IT CAN'T COME SOON ENOUGH!" the class bellowed. Every student in the lecture hall rose to their feet and gave a standing ovation. Archer decided right then and there that nothing was going to stop him on his way to becoming a winner. He was going to be the person to lead his generation's march toward the Day, and he would not be satisfied until he was number one on the scoreboard.

Archer left the lecture hall feeling better about himself. His life finally had genuine purpose, and he was ready to live it out. Rather than attending his other classes, he returned to his dorm room and logged on to his personal account to see his current HQ standing. "You have 475,917,400 points to your name. This places you in the 45.56th percentile in your nation," an automated voice said.

I've gotta move up, he thought. *Forty-fifth percentile makes me want to vomit.*

As motivation, he added a permanent live update of his HQ score and percentile to his laptop screen so he could see it at all times. Archer's newfound motivation drove him to begin reading articles online, written about society's winners. He wanted to know the secrets that allowed these people to rise to the top. Archer wished more than anything else in that moment to emulate them and capture their happiness and fulfillment. He observed his HQ score rise by a few points with each article he read. This positive feedback inspired him to search for more articles. Archer filled page after page in his notebook with tips on how to become a winner. Nothing was going to stop his ascendence to the top.

Ten hours flew by without Archer noticing.

"Hey, buddy!" Knox said as he walked in room.

"Oh, hey, Knox. What's up?"

"Not a whole lot,'" he replied. "I missed ya at dinner tonight. Did you not get my text?"

Archer had not looked at his phone all day nor had he eaten. "Uhh, no…I didn't get it. Must be the cell service in here," Archer said.

Knox looked at his phone. "That is so strange," Knox replied. "It says the text got delivered to you. Hmm, oh well. Stupid phone." Knox dropped the phone on his nightstand and fell onto his bed. "You look hard at work, Arch. Whatcha workin' on?"

Archer quickly shut his notebook. "Oh, just some…boring philosophy homework. I don't even want to start describing it, it's that boring." Archer did not wish to share any of his research with Knox.

"I hear ya. My classes are draggin' too," Knox said. "It's the dog days of the semester. That's for sure."

"Haha, yeah," Archer half-heartedly laughed, "I, uh, hear ya there."

The two looked at each other and then around the room.

"Well," Knox said, "don't let me interrupt your homework. I'm probably gonna hit the hay here soon."

"Sounds good," Archer said. "I'll probably be up a while longer. I hope that won't bother you."

Knox shook his head. "Nope, I could sleep through a twister rippin' right through the middle of our room. Don't you worry about me. Do what you gotta do, my friend."

"Thanks, pal," Archer said. Archer worked on an actual homework assignment until he was sure that Knox was asleep. He put his homework away once he heard a faint snore come from the other side of the room and began researching winners once again. "Wow, look at that house," he whispered to himself, looking at the mansion of a celebrity.

He closed his eyes and pictured himself pulling into the open-air garage in his brand-new, limited edition convertible sports car. He could see himself walking into the marble-floored foyer. "Mrs. Coleman is awaiting you in the kitchen, Mr. Coleman," his butler said to him.

"Thank you, Jeeves," Archer replied. "And what have you prepared for us this evening?"

"This evening, I have prepared your favorite meal: foie gras topped with the ultra-rare Italian white truffle with a side of caviar and escargot."

"That sounds divine. Thank you, Jeeves. If you'll excuse me, I will proceed to the kitchen," Archer said.

"As you wish, sir. Thank you, sir," Jeeves replied.

Archer walked between the foyer's two staircases to the kitchen.

"Darling!" his wife exclaimed.

"Hello, wife of mine!" he said.

"Oh, Archer, the children and I have awaited your arrival all the day long! We are oh so very happy to see you," she said as she kissed Archer on the hand.

"Yes, Father, we are oh so delighted to see you," his four children said in unison.

Archer smiled and patted the girl closest to him on the head. "Ahh, yes, I am pleased to be here as well. However, I must excuse myself as I desire a change of clothes before dining."

"Yes, of course, darling," his wife said. "Make yourself more comfortable."

"I shall indeed," Archer said as he exited the kitchen. Archer walked back to the foyer and admired the beautiful decorations.

"I forgot to mention, sir," Jeeves said. "Your art collection increased in value by one hundred million dollars today. I'll put you in touch with your investors to sort out potential deals you may wish to make after dinner.

"Thank you, Jeeves," Archer replied. "I could get used to this," he said to himself as he began to ascend the stairs. About halfway up, Archer realized that he was still a ways from the top. "Geez, how long is this staircase?" he said, starting to get winded. "That's the price you gotta pay for a tall house, I guess!"

Archer started to jog, but still, he made no progress. He stopped and noticed the stairs were moving downward like an escalator. "Yes, come back down, boy!" he heard from below. Archer looked down at the base of the staircase and witnessed a sharp dressed man in a pinstripe suit with piercing neon yellow eyes. "Come back, Archer! I have so much more to show you," he said.

"Who are you?" Archer asked as he began walking upward again.

"I am your friend, Archer. I wish to give you all your heart's desires."

"I don't believe you can do that," Archer replied.

The stairs began to move downward more quickly. The sharp dressed man laughed maniacally. "But I can!" he shouted. "Everything in my domain belongs to me, and I have the authority to dish it out as I please. Can't you understand this, boy?"

Archer increased his speed just to stay in place. "You never answered who you were!" Archer shouted.

"I am Antipalossssssss," he said as his forked tongue shot out of his mouth, "and I have the ability to make you happier than you ever dreamed before. Stop running away from me, my son."

Archer's spine shivered as he heard Antipalos call him his son.

"Submit to me, Archer. Stop spending all that useless energy trying to run away from me. You are getting nowhere, don't you see?"

Archer looked back and saw he was the same distance away from the man, even though he was now at a full sprint. "I don't think I should do that!" Archer yelled out.

"Archer, please!" he heard his wife say hysterically. "Quit running away from us!"

"Yeah, Daddy! Don't you love us?" a small child cried out.

Archer did not know what to say. "I do love you! At least I think I do!" he shouted.

"You *think* you love us?" the child said, crying even louder. "Daddy!"

Archer was becoming fatigued and slowed down. He could not keep up with the speed of the stairs.

"Embrace it!" Antipalos shouted. "You have nowhere to go but into my arms. I will care for you! All this and more shall be yours, if you just submit to me!"

Archer looked back and saw his wife and children standing in the middle of his beautiful mansion.

"Come down, Daddy!" he heard the children cry out.

Archer stopped, turned around to look them in their eyes. He couldn't resist any longer. He began to walk down the stairs.

"ARCHER, NO! DON'T FALL FOR IT! RUN AWAY BEFORE IT'S TOO LATE!" he heard Jeeves shout before tackling Antipalos. The two wrestled around on the floor.

"Get off of me, you fool!" Antipalos said as he picked Jeeves up by the front of his shirt and flung him across the room and into the wall. Artwork on the wall crashed down onto the floor around him.

"Jeeves!" Archer shouted as he hopped over the rail and fell onto the floor, a fair distance below. "Jeeves! Are you okay?"

Jeeves, dazed from hitting the wall, said, "Run, Archer! Run! Get out of here!"

Archer turned and saw Antipalos approaching him. "But he'll hurt you even more," Archer pointed out. "You've gotta come with me!"

Jeeves pushed him away. "I'll be fine. I'm being protected. Now go. Go! Run for your life!"

Without thinking, Archer weaved his way through his family, past Antipalos, and ran straight through the front door of the house and into a crowd of people where he crashed into a man. The two of them fell to the ground in a heap.

"What's your problem?" the man yelled as they both got up. The man began to push Archer.

"I'm sorry! I'm not looking for trouble!" Archer said as he tried to hold the man back.

"Oh yeah? Well you found trouble! Here's a mouthful of trouble!" he said as he made a fist to punch Archer.

Archer threw his hands over his face to protect himself from the blow. Archer did not feel the man's punch. He opened his eyes a couple seconds later to see Franklin holding the man's fist. Archer looked at his grandfather.

"All right, let's break it up, you two," Franklin said.

"But he—" the man exclaimed.

"I know," Franklin interrupted. "I saw the whole thing. It was merely an accident. Go on about your day."

"Yeah, but—"

"Go!" Franklin ordered.

The man looked at Archer and back at Franklin before walking away, mumbling curses under his breath.

"Thanks, Grandpa," Archer said, hugging Franklin.

"You're welcome, Archer. Sure was a stroke of luck that I happened to be in the neighborhood!" Franklin said with a wink.

"Ha… Yeah, sure was," Archer replied. "Where did I come from?" he asked.

"Take a look for yourself," Franklin replied, pointing.

Archer turned around and saw a blinking, green neon sign that read HQ on the building he had just escaped. "Oh," Archer said, "It was one of those buildings."

"Indeed," Franklin replied.

Archer looked on as streams of people entered and exited the building. "How did I end up in there if I don't remember going in?" Archer asked.

"I told you a while back that most people do not realize when such things happen," Franklin answered. "They often happen gradually and unconsciously, one might say. Fortunate for you, you've been granted the ability to attend such events in person and experience their deceitfulness firsthand."

"I sure don't feel fortunate," Archer replied. "That guy was terrifying!"

"Ahh," Franklin said. "You must have met the adversary."

"Is that the Antonio guy you warned me about?" Archer asked.

"Antipalos," Franklin said, correcting Archer.

Some people around Archer bowed as they heard his name uttered.

"Yes, he is the nasty, lying brute that I warned you about. What did you think of him?"

Archer thought back to the events in the building. "Well, first off, he was hideously ugly, like some kind of snake man. And second, he promised me the world, but I just felt like he was lying to me. Both times I've been in those buildings, I felt like they were manipulating me to get me to take their offer."

"A wise observation, Archer," Franklin said, "That is the game they play. They offer products for the price of the soul. In the end, what good is that?"

Archer thought about it. "I guess if all this is real, then it can't be a good thing to do a deal with reptile man."

"You're right," Franklin replied in a serious tone. "Losing control of one's soul to Antipalos is the worst transaction a person could possibly make. You're lucky to have escaped." Franklin put his arm on Archer's shoulder.

"Come, let's get out of the busy area. I've got more time to speak with you this time."

The two travelled away from the Marketplace to the beach where Archer was rescued once before. They sat down, watching the waves gently ebb and flow in front of them. "Grandpa, I'm just sick of it," Archer said. "Why do I have to be the kid that gets chosen to come here. I mean, I love seeing you, don't get me wrong, but every time I come here, it hurts me somehow, and I find myself in some kind of weird life-or-death situation."

"But you *are* in a life-or-death situation, Archer," Franklin replied. "Everyone is. It's just that very few people ever realize it. The battle for your soul is constantly taking place, whether you know it or not, and if I were you, I would be more upset if you ever became unable to return here."

Archer gazed silently at the water.

"Archer, realize that your soul is in grave danger. Need I remind you that there is eternal life once you've perished from your earthly life? Eternal meaning *forever*. Infinitely long. Never-ending."

Archer remained silent.

"Had you agreed to sign the contract in the HQ building, you would have been that much more devoted to Anitpalos. Now that you've been in his presence, is he someone who you wish to give your allegiance to for eternity?"

"Not in a million years," Archer quickly replied, remembering the cold, hate-filled look in his eyes.

"Good," Franklin replied. "That is very good." Franklin sat patiently with his grandson as he internalized all this new information.

Archer broke the silence. "Why doesn't anyone know all of this down on earth?"

"Some do," Franklin replied, "but they must operate in secret or else they will be banned or exiled, as I was."

The dots started to connect in Archer's mind. "I remember Mom and Dad mentioning that," Archer said. "They said you were America's Most Wanted criminal at one point."

"It's true," Franklin replied. "The HQ system put in place when I was a child, forced me on the run."

"Wait," Archer said, "you were alive when they introduced the HQ system? I always thought that happened like hundreds of years ago."

"They have deliberately led you to believe that," Franklin replied. "If you notice, your educators don't give many dates. The goal is to make the pre-HQ times as distant and archaic as possible in everyone's minds."

"I see," Archer said. "How old were you when they made those changes then?"

"I was eight years old when the system currently in place was codified into law," Franklin answered.

"Woah," Archer said. "What was life like before?"

Franklin thought for a moment. "Well," he said, "I was only a young boy, so I don't remember too much about it, but I would say the biggest difference was that my family and I would freely attend weekly meetings where we learned about this Transcendent realm and the King." Franklin bowed his head.

"In public? No way," Archer said.

"Yes," Franklin countered, "in public. It was open to anyone who wished to attend."

"I just can't wrap my head around that," Archer said.

"I understand why," Franklin sympathized. "You've never known it any other way. Anyway," Franklin continued, "the president's executive order and the new laws passed by Congress determined that these meetings were no longer permitted on the grounds of violating HQ, and anyone found in them would be punished accordingly. Dissident businesses were slowly closed and replaced with compliant businesses. Education fell under the DOW's jurisdiction, and they overtook philosophical thought, rewrote the textbooks, and punished all thought that disagreed with the HQ way of life."

"What was it like having your world change so drastically as a kid?" Archer asked.

"Immensely harmful," Franklin replied. "To be an eight-year-old and be forced to erase so much of what I had already learned was incredibly difficult to fathom in my young brain. To make matters worse, our family was religious. There was a major crackdown on those that refused to denounce their religious beliefs. People like us were called the 'Transcendentalists' because we believed that there was another realm outside of the physical realm. In fact, new federal laws at the time forced Transcendentalists to wear tags that easily broadcasted our identity, and thus our danger to society."

"Fascinating," Archer said.

"The new HQ system acquired a stronger grip on the nation through censorship and education as I progressed through school. The goal was not to debate the Transcendentalists, but rather to eliminate the discussion altogether. They made it clear that any discussion of a spiritual realm was treasonous and that life's meaning was easily found within the physical realities of earthly living."

"I see," Archer replied.

Franklin continued, "This was the function of the HQ system. A reward system based on points that informed society which actions were acceptable. In this way, Transcendent actions could be documented and resulted in subtraction of points because they were deemed the root cause of every ill society faced. The Transcendent realm needed to be destroyed, if humankind was to finally reach completion."

"The Day," Archer said.

"That's right," Franklin replied. "They called this the Day. At that point, my parents, your great-grandma and great-grandpa, began work as underground agents."

"Cool," Archer said. "What did they do?"

"I'm not sure," Franklin replied. "For the most part, they kept us kids out of their work, but they always found time, each day, to teach us about Transcendent matters. I can only imagine the good work they did for the kingdom before they got caught."

"Caught?"

"Yes. Caught and arrested by the authorities. I was barely a teenager when Mom and Dad were dragged away from the house by men dressed in all-black suits. I remember it like it was yesterday. By the end of the day, my siblings and I had been moved to separate towns and began our reeducation."

"Where did your parents get taken to?" Archer asked.

"We never found out. I never saw either of them again." Franklin continued, "I understand full well that no human system is without its faults, and the American system I was born into is no different. However, dissent toward our country was taken too far. The new system sought to delete the old nation. The old nation was diplomatically and peacefully replaced by a new nation, although the name remained the same. It was a slow and silent coup."

Archer listened intently.

"The new nation placed individual happiness and acceptance at the heart of their governance, as you've surely been taught. Anyone who was found to be guilty of opposing someone's pursuit of happiness was put in reeducation camps like the one my siblings and I attended. We were only allowed to return to regular school once we denounced our wrongdoing at the completion of the program."

"Did you?" Archer asked quickly.

Franklin became visibly upset. "I did denounce my faith in the King, in order to return to society. It was the greatest mistake of my earthly life." Franklin bowed his head and held it.

Archer could see how much this hurt his grandfather.

Franklin raised his head. "As I mentioned before, I denounced my faith at age thirteen, even though I was not fully indoctrinated by my reeducation. I wanted to be back in a school and find a group of peers that I fit in with in my new town. So I returned to school, made good grades and good friends. Slowly over time, I conformed to my peers and my education. I actually started to believe that the HQ system was my savior, my identity, and my god. It was a truly dangerous state of mind," Franklin said. "Thankfully at various times during high school, I would be swept to this very location to get a glimpse of the Truth. I was stubborn at first and didn't care to believe. My faith had already created so many problems in my young life. However, one of those times, I finally decided to meet the King," Franklin bowed, "just as you almost did on your last visit. I entered His gates, listened to what He had done for me, and I pledged my allegiance to Him right then and there."

"What had He done for you?" Archer asked.

"He saved my life, Archer," Franklin replied, "just like He saved yours."

"Well, did anything change when you pledged your allegiance to Him?" Archer asked.

"Everything changed," Franklin answered with a smile. "I was able to see eternal Truths manifested during my temporary stay in the Earthly realm. I also no longer had to behave in ways that earned me points to win. I simply lived for the King." Franklin bowed. "Through his actions, I had already won."

Franklin's testimony triggered an internal conversation in Archer's mind. *Suppose I do become the person with the most HQ points? I'd have the money and the mansion and the cars and the fame. Then what?'* Archer thought to himself. *I just die with all my stuff buried next to me? Where's the hope in that?*

Franklin's explanation of winning exposed the hollowness of winning by earthly standards, as portrayed by Professor Espinoza. Archer realized he could never be *fully* satisfied with a life of chasing accomplishments. He imagined the numerous sacrifices it would take to reach the top of the HQ leaderboard. *I'd most likely have very little time to spend with my family and friends. I'd probably miss my kids growing up. Oh man, think about the enemies I'd create on the way to the top. I bet there would be people around every corner trying to dethrone me as top dog. That wouldn't be fun to be constantly looking over my shoulder for the rest of my life. And worst of all, there is a 100 percent chance I'm going to die, and I'd be forced to pass on all my money and success to people who might not cherish it as much as I did. What if they blow all my money and ruin my empire I created? Would my accomplishments mean nothing at that point if nothing remains of them?*

Would it be like they never even happened? Like I was never even born?
Archer felt hopeless.

Franklin put his arm around his grandson. "What's going through your mind, son?"

Archer stared ahead blankly, trying to corral the thoughts running wild in his head. "Nothing matters," Archer finally said. "No matter what I do, it's never gonna be enough. Even if I have the most delicious meal on the planet, I'll be hungry again in a few hours. Even if I watch the best movie ever made, I'll want to watch another one. Meals and movies, or anything else that's good, can only make me satisfied for a little bit, and then I'll need more to satisfy me again. It's like I'm a hamster in a wheel. I won't ever be able to stop. Where's the finish line?"

Franklin grinned. "I'm so proud of you," he told Archer.

"For what?"

"You've discovered one of the wisest lessons that life has to offer to those that are willing to listen," Franklin replied.

"Which lesson is that?" Archer asked. "That trying to be filled completely by earthly life is just like running up an endless staircase, and no one will remember me once I'm gone? What a lousy lesson."

"Precisely that lesson, Archer," Franklin said. "Allowing those Truths to penetrate your soul is an action worth more than all of the world's gold. Can't you see that you're opening your mind to the possibility of jumping off the hamster wheel? You see that you can jump over the railing of the endless staircase like you did in the HQ building. This is the first step toward a life filled with joy and contentment."

"What am I supposed to do after I jump off?"

"You run," Franklin said.

"Where do I do run?" Archer asked.

"It's not *where* you run to, Archer. It's *who* you run to."

"And who do I run to?" Archer asked, already knowing what his grandfather was going to say.

Franklin smiled and said, "You run as fast as you can into the open arms of the King." Franklin bowed. "He is awaiting your arrival into His welcoming arms. Only He will be able to provide you the fullness and completion your soul desires. Earth's fleeting feelings of fullness give us a glimpse at the soul-filling goodness His Majesty offers."

Archer's soul flooded with hope. "That does seem to change everything," Archer said.

Franklin nodded in agreement.

"So," Archer said, "what did you do about all of this once you came back to your earthly self?" Archer asked.

"I took a risk, and I told a trusted friend at school about these visions. I had a feeling that I could trust him, and I was right. He said that he had visited the Transcendent realm a few times as well," Franklin replied. "We became best friends immediately and promised that we would never betray each other, no matter the consequences. He was a great man," Franklin said, solemnly.

"Anyway, there were rumors of a Transcendentalist underground faction, and we sought membership together. We were allowed entrance into one of their meetings once we had proven without a shadow of a doubt that we weren't spies sent by the local authorities."

"Were these the Truth Tellers?" Archer asked.

"Yes, this was the infamous Truth Tellers group that got me in so much trouble," Franklin said with a chuckle.

"And how old were you?"

"This all happened near the end of my senior year in high school. I spent over thirty years working for the Truth Tellers before I was forced on the run."

"I bet you've got some crazy stories from thirty years of work, huh?" Archer asked.

"Too many to count," Franklin replied, "even though all we ever did was spread the message of the King and His love for everyone." Franklin bowed. "We walked people through life's difficult questions like what you and I are doing right now. We loved these people through their difficulties and shared stories and eyewitness accounts about Him to those who wished to learn more. Most importantly we never forced anyone to stay who wished to leave. We just showed them the love and compassion that He had already shown us."

"But Mom and Dad said you used to kidnap people?" Archer asked.

"Many slanderous lies were spread about the Truth Tellers, including that one. It was all a plot to turn us into enemies of the state, a plot which overwhelmingly succeeded."

"I see," Archer said. "So what forced you out on the run?"

"Despite our best efforts to vet for spies, we let one slip in, and the operation I was leading at the time was ambushed. Most of my colleagues were arrested by the authorities, but I was one of the lucky few who got away. I knew at that point that I couldn't stay at home with the kids. I couldn't bear the thought of having them watch me get arrested and taken away like what I saw when I was young."

"I don't blame you," Archer said. "That had to have caused some kind of emotional scarring for you, right?"

"Most definitely," Franklin replied. "I had a recurring nightmare for most of my life where that scene would play repeatedly, but nothing I did could ever stop it. I would try and grab them as they were being dragged away, but my arms would go right through them like a phantom. I was completely useless."

"That's horrible," Archer said.

"You get used to it, unfortunately," Franklin replied.

"Did Grandma ever forgive you?" Archer asked.

"Of course she did," Franklin replied. "Your grandma understood that this was best for everyone's safety."

"Is that when she found out you were in the Truth Tellers?"

"Heavens no!" Franklin said. "Your grandma was in the Truth Tellers many years before I was. That's where we met and fell in love, truth be told."

"But Mom said she distinctly remembers Grandma berating you as you left them."

"It was all an act," Franklin said. "We decided together that the best way to protect our children was to pretend she had no idea. For better or worse, we decided to let our children find His Highness on their own terms. Society was growing increasingly vicious toward Transcendentalists. We ultimately trusted that He would provide them with a path to the kingdom. I often wonder if that was the right decision."

Franklin continued, "So for five years, with the help of some brave men and women, I bounced around from underground community to underground community, evading the authorities. Anyone caught assisting me was threatened with life in prison. I could never begin to repay those folks for the courage and hospitality they showed me." Franklin took a deep breath and exhaled slowly. "I was eventually caught one night, as we were preparing to relocate. The authorities placed a mole inside the Truth Tellers, and he informed them of my whereabouts that night. I was a sitting duck, Archer. They knew exactly where we would be. Myself and everyone with me were placed under arrest the moment we stepped outside, Oh, Archer, the guilt I felt for causing those poor people to be arrested was the worst torture I ever received."

"They tortured you?" Archer asked.

Franklin nodded his head up and down. "My friends and I were sent to a special reeducation camp and, yes, we faced intense hardship. Only with His Highness' strength were most of us allowed to persevere through it all. A few of us denounced our allegiance to Him to escape the pain, but the vast majority stayed faithful."

"You must really believe all of this to willingly endure that kind of harsh treatment," Archer said.

"That's the kind of strength you receive when you allow the Truth to reside in your heart," Franklin replied. "You and Him are an unstoppable force."

"Right," Archer said. "All right," Archer continued, "so you get arrested, and they try to break you, but that doesn't work. How did you end up on the farm if you never gave your allegiance to HQ?"

"Many years of good behavior and killing the guards with kindness," Franklin replied with a chuckle. "After a certain amount of time, the authorities determine that their techniques are not going to crack the prisoner. They have some scientific formula for it. I never understood it. Anyway, they figure that stubborn people like me better served society by working and providing utility for the community. That's a nice way of saying unpaid labor."

"Of course," Archer said.

"I accepted their plea deal and was sent to the countryside where I was given land and animals to live a bucolic life of solitude, providing food and wool to the community. I had never farmed in my life, so I faced a steep learning curve, but I was never one to shy away from a challenge."

"That explains why the cameras and microphones were all over the place."

"That was part of the deal. My every move was recorded. Well, almost every move."

"What do you mean? Like in the bathroom?"

"Unfortunately, they surveilled the bathroom as well," Franklin replied.

"Eww," Archer said.

"You're telling me," Franklin replied. "No, I discovered one blind spot on the whole of my property. No camera could see me when I stood on the western side of the old sycamore tree near the pond. This is where you enter the story, Archer."

"I do?" he asked excitedly.

"Yes, this is where you and I used to fish when you were just about this tall," Franklin said, holding his hand up to his waist. "It was there that you would share your dreams with me, and I realized that you were a special boy."

"Those were the best days of my childhood," Archer said, picturing himself on the edge of the water with a fishing pole.

"Those are some of my finest memories as well," Franklin replied, patting Archer on the back.

"Now," Franklin said, "you don't have much time before you have to go back. Do you remember how to get to my old farm?"

Archer nodded. "Of course I do. I could never forget!"

"Good," Franklin replied, "Listen carefully. I've buried a small metal box about three feet deep underneath that old sycamore tree on the western facing side. In it there are contents I believe you will find very useful. Do you promise me you'll find it?"

Archer's eyes lit up at the thought. "Yes! Of course I'll go find it!" he said. "It's like a real-life treasure hunt!"

"Indeed it is!" Franklin exclaimed. "And once you discover the treasure, you will want to sell everything you own to have it. I promise you of that."

"What's the treasure?" Archer asked.

"You'll have to find out for yourself," Franklin answered. "It wouldn't make sense if I told you right now."

"Come on," Archer begged. "Not even a hint?"

Franklin motioned like he was zipping his mouth shut. "All right," Franklin said, "it's time for you to head back. Before you leave, though, do you wish to visit the King?" Franklin bowed.

"Uhh, you know what? Maybe next time," Archer said. "I'm sure I'll be back soon, right?"

Franklin shrugged his shoulders. "It's not a risk I advise you to take, but you have every right to."

Archer nodded. "Let's just plan on next time then. By then, I'll have dug up your treasure, and maybe I'll feel compelled to go see the Big Guy."

"I pray that's the case," Franklin said. "Goodbye, Archer. Best of luck."

"Wait," Archer said. "How do I go back?"

"Just sit still and count to three," Franklin said as he reached toward Archer and lightly pushed his eyelids over his eyes.

"One, two, three," he said aloud. Archer opened his eyes. He lifted his head off his laptop and, trying not to awaken Knox, got in his bed and fell asleep.

CHAPTER 8

Noble Horses

"There's our big-time college student!" Nicole exclaimed as she embraced Archer.

"It's so good to see you!" Archer hugged his mother back. "I never thought I'd say this but…it's good to be back," he said with a smile.

"Son, welcome back," Henry said with an extended hand for a handshake.

"Thanks, Dad," Archer said as he shook Henry's hand. "I'm excited to be here for a couple weeks and hang out with you two and Jamie and Adrian. I haven't seen Adrian in ages!"

"Neither have we," Nicole said. "He barely calls or texts us when he's away. I'm surprised he's actually coming back for winter break."

"That's because he's a busy man," Henry said. "We'll just have to enjoy him while he's given us the time. Not too many people can pull off being a PhD student in HQ engineering and have a high-paying government job waiting on him once he graduates, *thanks to his old man*," he mumbled out the side of his mouth, "all while continuing to be a social influencer who has skyrocketed into the top fifth percentile of the HQ. It's all very impressive. Have you seen how many followers he has, Archer? It's incredible!"

The three walked into the kitchen and sat down at the dinner table. "Nope," Archer said. "I haven't watched any of his posts in a long time. I deleted my social media accounts this semester."

Nicole and Henry gasped.

"And why would you do such a thing like that?" Henry asked.

"Well I wanted to free up more time to study and use my time more wisely. It's actually been kinda nice not worrying about what to post."

Henry shook his head in disappointment. "Son, we raised you with better manners than that. It's common decency to take the time to let everyone know what you're doing in life. Think about your cousins and aunts and uncles! Oh my word, think about Aunt Betty! I bet she can't sleep at night! She worries so much about you kids!"

"You're overreacting, Dad," Archer said. "It's not like I'm one of those criminals they force to live offline. I still have a phone that people can call or text me on anytime, if they want to catch up."

"You don't understand, Archer," Henry explained. "It's more than that. Think about the missed HQ points! How can people upvote you in their surveys, if they can't see all your successes in life? And besides, I heard a rumor at work that Congress is about to pass a new law that will ban the deletion of social media accounts."

"Are they really going through with it?" Nicole asked.

"That's what I heard through the grapevine!" Henry said. "So, Archer, I think it would be wise to get ahead of the curve and hop back online before any of these changes happen."

"How about this?" Archer replied. "You let me know when that gets pushed through, and then I'll think about it. Why would I want to go back to playing the comparison game of social media when I have more peace now than I've ever felt?"

"Peace?" Henry asked. "Peace? What is that college of yours, *that I am paying $160,000 a semester for, mind you,* teaching you about peace? I ought to report them for that kind of indoctrination!"

"Woah, woah, woah! Calm down, Dad," Archer exclaimed. "Helmuth teaches according to the approved curriculum. They pretty much write the curriculum. 'Happiness is reality' posters are plastered all around campus, just like everywhere else. I just, you know, wanted a break from it all. At least for a little bit, just to see what it was like, and it turns out that I kind of like it."

Nicole could see that her husband was visibly upset. She attempted to ameliorate the situation. "It's okay, Henry," she said. "Sometimes kids don't understand quite what their actions mean. He's still just a child, you know. He's got plenty of time to—"

"Plenty of time?" Henry said. "No one has plenty of time! The boy can take 'a break' when he's dead! We only get so much time on this earth, and then, *poof*, we die. Game over, man!"

Archer was scared of the tone his father was using.

"I've busted my back and dedicated my whole life to succeeding so that my family can have a better life than I had. That's what this whole system is about. It's tried, it's tested, and it *works*!" he said, pounding the table. "And I will not have my son march in here and tell me that he is so selfish that he can't put his ego aside for one stinking minute to think about the hellish repercussions of his actions."

Archer sarcastically laughed at his father's comments. "Hellish, huh?" Archer asked. "Well I'm sorry that I could never be *Adrian 2.0* like you always wanted me to be! Let me live my life how I see fit, and I'll do the same for you. How's that sound, Henry?"

Henry was silent. His expression turned from fire and passion to cold and blank.

"Honey?" Nicole asked. "What's going on?"

"Yeah, Dad. You look frozen."

He did not respond.

Nicole nudged Henry's shoulder. "Talk to us, Henry."

Henry took a deep breath and exhaled slowly. "I know what's going on," he finally said. "Yup. It all makes sense now."

"What? What makes sense?" Nicole asked.

Henry sat silent for another moment before speaking. He turned to his wife. "I never fully trusted you, Nicole. And now I know my suspicions were RIGHT!" he yelled, spit flying from his mouth.

Nicole began to tear up. "I have no idea what you're talking about, Henry! Why would say such a thing?"

"YOU CAN'T TALK TO MOM LIKE THAT!" Archer screamed out as he stood up.

"You'd better close your mouth and sit down if you know what's good for you, boy," Henry said calmly, pointing his index finger menacingly at Archer.

Deflated, Archer sat back down.

Henry stood up from his seat at the table. "I know what you did, Nicole. I was going to wait until the break was over to bring it up, but I just can't wait any longer. Archer's little act of rebellion was the final piece of the puzzle."

"Please," Nicole said, "explain what you're talking about!"

"I'm talking about this!" Henry exclaimed as he pulled out Franklin's letter to Archer that was in his pocket.

Blood rushed to Nicole's face, and her cheeks turned a deep red hue.

"Didn't think I would ever find it, did you?" he asked, holding up the letter in Nicole's face. "You know? I always had something telling me deep down inside that you kept Franklin's propaganda letters. I should have never let you take care of disposing them." Henry got nose-to-nose with Nicole and yelled, "WHERE ARE THE REST OF THEM?"

Nicole immediately pushed his face away from hers.

"GET AWAY FROM HER!" Archer shouted as he stood up from the table.

Henry turned his attention away from Nicole and glared at his son.

Archer looked directly into his cold, hate-filled eyes.

Suddenly Henry lunged toward Archer from across the table.

"Henry!" Nicole shouted, grabbing his leg.

"YOU TALK A BIG GAME! LET'S RUMBLE, BIG BOY!" Henry screamed at Archer.

Archer backed up from the table, out of his father's reach.

Nicole was trying her best to keep him at bay.

"LET GO OF ME, WOMAN!" he said, kicking her.

Archer decided that enough was enough. The perfect opportunity presented itself to hit Henry as hard as he could. His father was positioned halfway on the kitchen table, with Nicole attempting to hold his legs. Henry was turned away from Archer, attending to

Nicole. Archer reached for a plate off the table to smack his father in the head with. He raised it above his head.

"Archer, no!" Nicole yelled.

Henry turned around in time to block the strike. "Now you're in *big* trouble, mister!" Henry yelled. "Come here!"

Ding-dong. "Hellooooo!" Jamie said from the front door. "Your two favorite children are here!"

Archer and his parents immediately stopped what they were doing. Henry quietly lowered himself back to the ground with Nicole's assistance. Archer placed the plate back in its rightful place on the table, as the three of them quickly tidied up the dining room to remove all traces of the altercation.

"This never happened," Henry whispered to Archer and Nicole as everyone sat back down.

"Hey! There they are!" Henry said, walking over to Jamie and Adrian as they entered the dining room. "We were wondering when you two would get here!" Henry said with a big smile.

"So yeah, this is my parents' house," Adrian said into his phone. "Pretty lame, but it's got kind of a cool retro thing going on, so—"

"Who's he talking to?" Archer asked.

"Shh!" Jamie said. "He's livestreaming to his three million followers."

Henry mouthed the word *wow* exaggeratedly.

Adrian walked through the kitchen without acknowledging his family. "So this is where I used to eat dinner way back when. Hahaha! What a loser I was back then. I was probably in the bottom fiftieth percentile or something. Yuck," he said, sticking his tongue out. "All right, my Adrian Apostles. The moment you all voted you were most excited to see! I will now take you guys up to my old bedroom to see just how *lame* I was." Adrian walked upstairs.

Archer looked around the room at his family. "What just happened?" he asked.

"It's called talent," Jamie replied. "You'd recognize it if you had any."

"Wait a minute," Archer shot back. "How come you can recognize it then?"

"Ha. Ha," Jamie said sarcastically. "Veeerrrry funny, wise guy. Very funny."

"Thank you," Archer replied proudly.

"You're not welcome," she said. "I'll have you know I just got chosen to be in an off-Broadway production of *Freedom Fighters: The Musical*."

Henry and Nicole's eyes lit up.

"Wow, honey! That's amazing news!" Nicole exclaimed.

"Our little girl is gonna be a star!" Henry said.

"Think about the HQ points I'll get!"

They walked over to Jamie and hugged her.

"Let's hold on for a second," Archer said, still seated. "Just what role did you get?"

Jamie paused for a moment. "Well, you see, Archer, acting is much more than just the words spoken. Oftentimes, it's the ambience created that is the true star of the show."

Archer narrowed his eyes. "Riiiiight. Ambience. Got it. Can you inform us what exactly is the name of the character that you're playing?"

"Officevendingmachine#5," she mumbled.

"What was that? I couldn't hear you?" Archer asked.

"Office vending machine number five! I'm dressed up as a vending machine in the break room scene where they write down the first HQ algorithm on a napkin, okay! The specific role I got and how few lines—"

"Zero," Archer interjected. "Zero lines. Vending machines don't talk."

Jamie sighed. "Yes, the specific role I got and having zero lines is not important."

"Seems kind of important to me," Archer interrupted.

"Let your sister talk!" Nicole ordered.

"Thank you, Mother," Jamie replied. "Look, the point is I got a role on stage where all eyes will be on me and, afterward, I'll be signing autographs for all my adoring fans."

Archer opened his mouth to speak, but Nicole put her finger up to her mouth to shush him before he could say anything.

"Well that is just amazing, Jamie," Henry said. "Your mother and I are so proud of you." He turned to Archer. "Archer, say something nice to your sister."

"Fine," Archer said. "Jamie, I'm really happy for you. This has been a long time coming."

"Thank you, Archer," she replied.

Archer continued, "And, hey, with hard work and dedication, you might work all the way up to office vending machine number two in a couple of years!"

Jamie smiled. "Aww, Archer. That's really sweet of you to say."

Nicole put her finger up to her mouth to silence Archer again.

Jamie yawned and stretched her arms out. "Oh man," she said. "I'm beat from the long drive back," Jamie said. "I think I'm just going to hit the hay early tonight."

"Already?" Henry asked. "We barely got to chat with you!"

"I'm no use once I'm sleepy," Jamie said, yawning again. "You know this."

"I understand," Henry said. "But you're still gonna show me how to change my selfie filters tomorrow, right?"

"Of course, Daddy!" Jamie exclaimed. "I'd do anything to help you up your selfie game. Your ones now are so embarrassing! Yuck!"

"That they are!" Henry said. "More likes and comments, here I come!"

"Archer," Jamie said, turning to her brother, "would you be a doll and carry my bags to my room?"

"But that's my room now," Archer said.

"Ah, ah, ah," Jamie replied. "It was my room first. Seniority rules."

"Well," Archer said, "you've got crow's feet like a senior citizen, so I guess I can't argue there."

"Enough!" Nicole said. "Help your sister carry her…*eight* bags…to her room. You can sleep on the couch."

"Fine," Archer said begrudgingly.

Archer and Jamie walked to the front door where her bags were lying.

"Still enjoying the big city?" Archer asked as he picked up some of Jamie's travel bags. "Goodness, Jamie! What do you have in here? I can barely lift them!"

"Archer, darling," she said, "you don't look this good without a little help from the makeup and wardrobe department."

"Or a lot of help," Archer mumbled under his breath. Archer struggled up the stairs and dropped the bags on Jamie's bedroom floor with a big *thud*! "Phew," Archer said, out of breath, "I didn't think I was gonna make it."

"Ahh, the old bedroom," she said, ignoring Archer. "Thinking about all the memories I made in here really takes me back: all the sleepovers, all the movie nights, all the boys—" Jamie covered her mouth with her hands.

"Oh really?" Archer asked.

"Uhh," Jamie replied, "you didn't let me finish! What I was about to say was all the boysenberry ice cream we used to eat together! You of all people should know that's always been my favorite!"

"Smooth," Archer said.

Just then, Adrian barged into Jamie's bedroom. "And the final room in the grand tour is my sister Jamie's bedroom, which later became my little bro Archer's bedroom. Say hi to the good people, siblings!" He pointed the phone toward Archer and Jamie.

"Hello, lovelies!" Jamie shouted as she shoved Archer out of the frame. "We love you all! Don't forget to follow me on all social medias! My username is—"

"Okay, okay, let's not bore my audience," Adrian interrupted. "Let them fall asleep on their own." Adrian pointed his phone toward Archer. "Everyone, this is Archer," he said. "He's a little rough around the edges, but you'll come to know and love him just as much as I do!" he said, hugging Archer with their cheeks smashed together. "Well don't be shy, Arch," Adrian said. "Say something to the people!"

"Something to the people," Archer replied.

"Oh you haven't changed a bit," Adrian said as he pinched Archer's cheek.

Adrian pointed the phone toward his face. "All right, the time has unfortunately come to end the stream. It's time to say good night, my Adrian Addicts," Adrian said. "I hope your dreams are filled with Adrian. His will be filled with you! Muuuuwah!" he said, blowing a kiss.

Archer rolled his eyes.

Jamie watched in adoration.

"Phew," Adrian said, wiping his forehead, "I really had to work hard to make this dump seem somewhat entertaining to all those idiots." Adrian belly flopped onto the bed and rolled over on his back. "Well, well, well," he said, "looks like we got the old band back together! Oh, I've got so much to catch you two up on in my life."

"You are amazing, Adrian," Jamie replied. "How do you have time to make all your content? It must be exhausting!"

"Oh, Jamie, you don't even know the half of it," he replied. "I'm so busy I can't even get a moment to catch my breath! But first, because I am such a good person, I'd like to hear how little Archer's first semester of college went! Spill the beans, man! What are they having you learn over at that landfill disguised as a college?"

Adrian was currently attending Helmuth's rival college, Engels University.

"Well," Archer said, "I've learned a lot in my Philosophy 111 class. I'm a philosophy major, if you didn't know, so it kinda makes sense why it's my favorite class right now."

Adrian perked up. "Oh I am so glad to hear that, Archer. We all wondered when you would come to your senses and get interested in something important."

"Thank you?" Archer said, sensing the backhanded compliment.

"Anyway," Adrian said, "I'll have to hear more about it tomorrow because this star is ready to head to bed for the night."

"Oh okay," Archer said, disappointed. "I thought we were just getting started."

"Archer, you sweet, naive little boy," Adrian said. "Perfection like this requires *at least* nine hours of beauty rest. We'll chat more tomorrow after my post-wake up, post-shower, post-dressing, pre-breakfast livestream. Good night, siblings!"

"Goodnight, Adrian," Archer and Jamie said as he walked out of the room.

"Has he always been this big of a jerk? Or is that something new?" Archer asked. "I can't quite remember."

"Please, Archer," Jamie replied. "You wish you had a tenth of the attention he gets on a daily basis. You're just, too, proud to admit it."

"No chance," Archer said, laughing.

"There's the pride I was talking about," Jamie said, yawning.

"All right, get out of here so I can get *my* beauty rest. Besides, I think I hear the couch calling your name."

"Whatever you say," Archer said. "Good night, Jamie." Archer walked down the stairs and saw Nicole sobbing on the couch.

Archer suddenly remembered the altercation with Henry. "What did he do to you?" Archer asked sharply as he sat down by his mother.

"Nothing, honey," she replied. "He—he just left. He got in his car and left. I tried to stop him and ask where he was going, but I couldn't get a word out of him. He wouldn't even look at me," Nicole said, through tears and sniffling.

Archer tried to comfort his mother. "I've never seen Dad that angry," Archer said. "Has he had these tantrums before?"

"I've only seen him like this a couple times before," Nicole replied. "Never toward me, though."

"He'd better not," Archer replied. "By the way," Archer said. "If you don't mind me asking, why *did* you keep Grandpa's letter for me?"

"I...I...," Nicole struggled, "I just heard something inside me say that I should keep it for you. I've never experienced anything like it since. I like thinking it was my dad, but I just don't think that's possible. Am I crazy for thinking that?"

"No, I don't think you're crazy at all. In fact," Archer said, checking his surroundings to make sure they were alone, "I have something to tell you that's even crazier, but you have to promise me you won't tell anyone else. Do you promise?"

"You have my word as your mother."

Archer took a deep breath and looked around again. "For the past couple of years, I've been speaking with Grandpa," he said.

Nicole laughed. "What are you talking about, honey? He passed away years ago. That's ridiculous!"

"No, it's true!" Archer replied.

Nicole did not believe him. "Archer, I saw his body in the casket with my own eyes, and then we buried him out at his farm. Don't you remember? We were all there. I don't know what you would mean by 'speaking with Grandpa.'"

"To be honest," Archer said, "I don't fully understand either, but I've been having visions where I feel like I'm transported to another world where he is. It sounds so stupid when I say it out loud, but I promise you that it's really happening."

"So a dream," Nicole stated.

"No," Archer replied. "It's not just a dream. It's more."

Nicole shook her head with a concerned look on her face.

"I know, I know," Archer said. "Look, I have a way to prove to you that everything I'm saying is real."

"Let's hear it," Nicole said, crossing her arms.

"Okay," Archer said, "Grandpa told me about a box that he buried at his farm. He told me exactly where it was. If I go, and it's there, then we'll know for a fact that he's been talking to me. Do you think you can help me?"

"Archer, I don't think you quite know the amount of trouble you can get in by saying these things," Nicole replied. "Talking with the dead? That's a serious violation of HQ."

"I know, Mom," he said. "But wasn't it you that said, one day, a parent has to take their hands off and let their kid scrape their knee sometimes?"

"Yes, but I didn't say that a parent should let their kid become a criminal! There's a line, Archer."

"Of course there is," Archer replied. "And I love that you care so much about me, but I *need* you to trust me on this one. Just let me look for the box. If it's not there, this is the last you'll ever hear about anything of the sort. Please."

Nicole thought about Archer's proposition.

Let Archer go. Nicole heard. Her mouth opened wide in surprise. "What just happened?"

Archer asked, looking around, "Why are you looking like that?"

"You have to go look for it," she replied.

Archer leaned toward Nicole. "Really? You're gonna let me go, just like that?"

"As much as I don't want you to, I heard it," Nicole said. "It said, 'Let Archer go.'"

Archer nodded his head in agreement. "Thank you!" he said, hugging Nicole. "I'll explain more to you later but, for now, this conversation never happened, okay?"

"Okay," Nicole said. "Just be safe, Archer. That's all I ask."

Ding-dong. "Hellllooooo, family!" Henry said from the front door.

Nicole wiped all evidence of tears from her face and got up from the couch to greet Henry.

"Henry! I was worried you wouldn't be back for the night."

"Oh, honey," Henry said, kissing her on the cheek. "Don't worry. I was just out getting the toilet paper you asked me to get, remember? It's your favorite!"

"Yes! Of course," Nicole said, slapping her forehead. "How could I forget the, uh, toilet paper? Oh, thank you, dear. Here, I'll take that and put it up. You really are just the best!"

"Haha! No, honey. *You're* the best," he said as he kissed her again. "Oh and Archer," Henry said.

"Yeah, Dad?" Archer asked.

"I can't wait to hear about your studies. I love you, and I hope you sleep well, son."

"Oh," Archer said, "uhh, thanks. I love you too. Have a good night."

Henry walked back to his bedroom, whistling as he went. Nicole and Archer shot each other a brief look before she left for her bedroom as well.

The next morning, Archer found himself lying awake on the couch before any of his family members had woken up. He started to formulate a plan to retrieve the box on Franklin's property. *Number one priority*, he thought to himself, *do not let Dad find out.* Winter break was to last two weeks, so he decided the best time to act would be toward the end of his stay. *How can I get away from my family without them suspecting a thing, though?* he thought. *Ty! That's it! I'll say I'm going to hang out with Ty to see how his semester went. Genius. I'll make the half hour drive to the farm, dig up the treasure that awaits me, and then*—Archer's mind went blank. *And then what?* he thought to himself. *If Grandpa is right, then there's no way I could go back to college. I couldn't tell Mom and Dad that, though. They'd kill me!* Archer couldn't think of a plan that left him satisfied. *I guess just take it one step at a time,* he settled on. *See what's in the box, if there is one, and go from there. That's the only option I've got right now.*

"Oh," Henry said, startled, "good morning, son. I didn't expect you to be up so early."

"Good morning, Dad," Archer replied. "Where are you off to?"

Henry was caught off guard by his son's question. "Well, Archer, I'm, uhh, off to work!" he said. "Someone's gotta keep the lights on around this place, you know!"

"But it's Saturday. You've never worked on the weekend."

Henry's eyes darted back and forth. "Uhh, well, there's this, uhh, emergency project me and the gang are working on that's urgent. Yes, reaaalllll urgent. So we got called in to work today. Darn the luck. All I want to do is be here all day with you kids!"

"How come you're not in your work uniform?" Archer asked.

"Oh well, there's a simple and obvious explanation for that which…is…that…we don't have to wear them on the weekend! Yup! That's the reason!"

Archer did not believe his father. "It's a real shame you have to work today. I sure was looking forward to hanging out with you."

"Me too, son," Henry replied.

"But you know what, Dad?" Archer said as he narrowed his eyes. "This is just so *you*. You are willing to do *anything* for this family. They don't make hard workers like you anymore, you know? When duty calls, there's goes Henry! Henry! Henry! He's our man! If he can't do it, no one—"

"All right, all right," Henry said with a fake chuckle. "I get your point, son. It seems like you're thinking I'm putting work ahead of you, and I get it. But one day, you'll be a father, and you'll understand that sometimes work comes at the worst times and loving your family means sacrificing for them."

"You should have been a politician," Archer whispered under his breath.

"What was that?" Henry asked.

"Oh nothing, Father. I was just saying that I hope you have the most wonderful of days at work," Archer said with a large, fake smile.

"Thanks, son," Henry said. "Tell the others that's where I'm at, won't you?"

"Of course I will, Father," he replied. "Now run along before you hit traffic! We wouldn't want that, now would we? Come on! Out you go! Toodle-oo!"

Henry picked up his briefcase and made a beeline for the door without saying another word.

"Who left?" Adrian said as he came down the stairs.

"Just Dad," Archer replied. "He said there's an emergency at work."

"So it's not an intruder?" Adrian asked.

"No," Archer said, laughing.

"False alarm," Adrian said, looking into his phone. "Sorry to scare all of you with my surprise burglar stream, everyone. I appreciate the support from the live chat, though. I don't know how I would have gotten through this without you, my adoring fans!"

"But nothing happened," Archer said. "It was just Dad leaving."

"Oh, Henry," Adrian said. "Putting in the hard hours at work."

Archer laid back down in frustration.

"And that," Adrian declared into his phone, "is how I will leave you all this morning: With the image of a hardworking American father, *my* hardworking American father, doing what he has to do for his family. I guess that's where I get my incredible work ethic from, huh? Comment in the section below if you think I'm right about that. Okay, goodbye for now, Adrian Army. Remember to like and subscribe before my postlunch, preafternoon nap livestream for a chance to win a signed copy of my memoir. Ta-ta!"

Archer nearly pulled an extraocular muscle rolling his eyes so violently.

"I guess now that I'm up, I might as well stay up," Adrian said, walking toward the couch. "Good morning, little brother. You're welcome for including you in my livestream."

"Gee, thanks," Archer said unenthusiastically.

"Hey, you know what?" Adrian said, "I'll even tag you in the video description. Think of all the followers you'll get from it! Oh, I am such a good person! What are your social media usernames?"

"I actually don't have any," Archer replied. "I deleted them during the semester."

Adrian looked at his brother in disgust. "You did what?"

"I deleted them all," Archer said. "Every. Single. One. What do you think about that?"

Adrian had to sit down to avoid fainting.

"Are you okay, Adrian?"

"Yes, I'll be fine. A little triggered, but I'll be fine. I'm a warrior."

"Oh I know," Archer said sarcastically.

Adrian shook his head back and forth to regain full strength. "What could possibly lead you to do such a nasty thing like delete your social media accounts?" Adrian asked.

"Well, it was taking up a lot of my time and brainpower," Archer replied. "Plus people only post about things that go well for them. I know the lowlights in my life, and so when I saw my stream that's filled with everyone else's highlights, I felt terrible about myself."

Adrian shook his head even faster. "Archer, Archer, Archer," he said. "Letting others see just how perfect your life is the whole point! Need I remind you that a large chunk of your HQ score depends on how many people upvote you on their surveys? How else do you think I rack up so many HQ points a day? I'm everywhere!"

Archer opened his mouth to speak but was cut off.

"And besides," Adrian said, "comparison drives us to be better versions of ourselves! I know it does for me. When I see someone with more followers than me, it just eats me up inside, and I don't stop working until I've got more than them. It's how humans have always operated, Archer." Adrian could tell that Archer wasn't buying it.

"Look," he continued," I'll be your personal HQ manager for the next few days while we're both here. Your attitude is poor, but you've got potential, Archer. I can see you've got what it takes to be a winner. Take it from me: someone so close to being a winner that I can taste it! Gosh, I am such a giving person!"

"Who decides when you're officially a winner?" Archer asked with air quotes.

Adrian scoffed. "You don't know this already? You're more of a lost cause than I thought. Haven't you ever heard of the Board of Winners?"

"No," Archer replied.

Adrian pinched the bridge of his nose. "Keep it together, Adrian." He sighed and continued, "The Board of Winners is a highly exclusive 'Who's Who' of influencers that vote on who has 'won at life.' Once you receive enough votes, they send you a pure gold crown with the inscription 'Winner' engraved on it. Here, let me show you." Adrian searched online for a picture of the crown. "Ahh, here it is. I forgot that it's only allowed to be shown on the Board of Winners' official page. Look."

Archer looked at the golden crown with jewels on Adrian's phone.

"How come winners don't get to post a picture with it?" Archer asked.

Adrian began to laugh. "Oh, Archer. That's the beauty of being a winner. You get to a point where you don't have to prove yourself anymore. You've already won! If you're posting about being a winner, then you are *definitely not* a winner."

"So how do know there actually are winners out there if no one admits it?" Archer asked.

"Come on, Arch," Adrian replied. "It's pretty obvious. The rich are winners—"

Archer interrupted, "Yeah, but how rich?"

"Well," Adrian replied, "rich enough. You just know it when you get there. Look, the point is, celebrities are winners—"

Archer interrupted again, "Yeah, but how famous do you have to be?"

Adrian scoffed again. "You know, Archer, I'm starting to think you need a serious talking to."

"Oh yeah? About what?" Archer asked indignantly.

"About everything. This whole thing we call life," Adrian said, motioning his arms over his head.

"Fine!" Archer said. "Let's do it! I love philosophical talks."

"Perfect!" Adrian exclaimed. "Where at?"

"How about we go get some coffee at Java Guevara down the road?"

"Sounds good to me," Adrian said. "Give me a minute though, I need to change into my social clothes. There is no way I'm going to go out in public looking like this. The paparazzi would have a field day!"

The two boys drove to the coffee shop and sat down at a booth.

"All right, Adrian," Archer said, sipping his drink, "let's hear what you have to say."

"Wait a minute, Arch," Jamie replied. "I've gotta get a good pic of my cappuccino." *Click.* "Social media drinks first!"

"How are we from the same parents?" Archer asked rhetorically.

"Annndddd...posted!" Adrian said. "All right, Archer. Let's get to it. How can Big Brother help you?"

Archer thought for a moment. "How about we start with happiness?" Archer said.

"Brilliant!" Adrian said. "What about it?"

"Well, I've been wondering lately if it's possible to ever be truly happy."

Adrian took a sip of his drink. "Wow, you're not messing around, are you?" Adrian replied. "Well, the short answer to your question is yes. That's the point of being a winner. You've made it to the top, and everyone sees how good your life is. Haven't you been learning this stuff in your college courses?"

"I mean, I have," Archer said, "but sometimes I doubt it."

"You doubt it?" Adrian said as he was about to spit out his drink. "Keep it down, Archer! You shouldn't be saying things like that! Next you're gonna tell me you think there's an afterlife!"

Archer looked at his brother and suddenly realized he wasn't denying it fast enough. "Yeah...that would be stupid," Archer said. "Of course, I wouldn't say that. I'm just saying that sometimes I feel like a loser playing this whole HQ game, and I can't see a way where I ever stop feeling like one."

Adrian nodded up and down. "I know what's wrong with you," he replied. "Your type needs to be shown the reasons why things are the way they are. You don't just believe things on faith, and I respect that."

My type? Archer thought to himself.

Adrian continued, "I think a little history lesson is just what the doctor ordered. Let's go back to the beginning. Once upon a time, humans believed in silly gods," Adrian explained. "According to them, these gods protected them, made their food grow, and even rolled the sun over the sky each day. This system of belief worked for a really long time until all those gods got combined into one super God. This God evolved over time into an omniscient, omnipresent being."

"Okay?" Archer asked. "What does that have to do with anything?"

"What I'm getting at," Adrian said, "is these pagans thought super God was their source of happiness. They believed this singular God was what they called 'benevolent' and that He was only capable of doing good in people's lives. And get a load of this, Arch. They really thought that super God structured the universe on purpose for the benefit of humanity! What a riot!"

Sounds kind of like the King, Archer thought to himself.

"Don't you see the contradictory nature of their beliefs?" Adrian asked. "How is an all-loving, all-knowing super God able to create a world around us with so much evil?"

"That's a good question," Archer replied. "I had never really thought about that."

"Of course you hadn't," Adrian said. "Thanks to the Freedom Fighters, we've been freed from wasting our time thinking about such nonsense!"

Archer tried to answer all these accusations in his head with what he had learned about the King from Franklin. However, he couldn't. Adrian's accusations seemed like undeniable proofs against the King.

"Here's another brainteaser for you," Adrian said. "Why hasn't He already eradicated evil? If He's all-loving and all-powerful, He would want no evil in the world and simultaneously have the ability to get rid of it for us. But we see bad things happening all the time! Are your eyes lying to you? Of course not. This means either He could take away evil and chooses not to, in which case He's not benevolent, or He doesn't have the ability to take away evil, in which case He's not omnipotent."

Archer remained silent.

"If we continue this thought experiment," Adrian explained, "we realize that anyone with half a brain can see it means that He's neither benevolent nor omnipotent. Go even further, and you easily see that super God is pure fiction. Do you know what this means?"

"No," Archer said quietly.

"It means the world has no meaning without any gods or super God running the show," Adrian said. "We finally discovered that things don't happen for a reason. That's just a silly saying that people used to say to help them get through tough times. In other words," Adrian continued, "life doesn't run on an if-then plane. An organized Creator would have created an organized universe in an if-then manner. If you do what pleases it, you will receive blessings. If you don't do what pleases it, you will be punished. But we obviously don't see that."

"I guess that's true," Archer said, thinking about all the bad things he had done and gotten away with.

"Therefore," Adrian continued, "this proves that the only realm of being is the physical realm. Super God was slain, once and for all, by the Freedom Fighters. Humans were freed from religious bondage and were now beholden only to themselves and their desires. We no longer have to suffer and sacrifice for the blessings of some stupid, made-up God in the sky anymore. Suffering and pain can now be truly seen for what they are: things to be avoided all costs. And vice versa: pleasure is to be sought at all times. We're free to spend our time and energy pursuing what makes us happy. Cheers to that!" Adrian raised his drink toward Archer.

Archer unenthusiastically touched Adrian's cup with his.

"Does that answer your question about happiness?" Adrian asked.

"Sorta," Archer replied. "But what if suffering and pain can be good for you? And what if pleasure can be bad for you?"

"How on earth could that be possible?" Adrian asked.

"It's like you said earlier: what if the hurt of losing or the sting of comparison motivates someone to work harder? Or even better! What if they want to use their own time and energy to prevent someone from feeling that way?"

"Those are some big what-ifs!" Adrian replied. "Can I return the favor with some what-ifs of my own?"

"Go for it," Archer said.

"What if you died tomorrow?" Adrian asked. "You personally did not gain anything from that time and energy you spent preventing someone else's from suffering. You did not live to see the fruits of your labor, so there's no way it was worth the trouble. Your argument also contradicts itself because you are saying that suffering can be advantageous to a person. If that is the case, then why would you prevent someone from suffering, thereby hindering their growth? And the same goes for pleasure, just in the reverse. Pleasure is obviously good, so why would anyone prevent pleasure for themselves now when the future is unknown? What we know is today. Not tomorrow or the day after."

"Okay, if that's the case," Archer said, "then why does anyone save money? If today is all we know, then why don't we spend it all for pleasure today?"

"Good question," Adrian said. "There's a fine line between responsibility and philosophy. We have a responsibility to our fellow human beings to not be a burden on others. Saving money ensures that we will be able to pay for our own things in the future. Furthermore, money can grow bigger and bigger through compound interest so the more you have, the quicker your bank account grows.

Being richer makes us feel safer, happier, and more important. This is why net worth is weighed so heavily in our HQs."

Dang, he's good, Archer thought in his head. "All right," Archer said, "that brings up another question."

"Keep 'em coming," Adrian replied.

"I heard someone say, once in middle school, that the winners don't feel like winners at the top," Archer said. "In fact, rumor has it that they're just as unhappy as everyone else."

"Blasphemy!" Adrian shouted. "Who told you that? They ought to be reported to the authorities!"

Archer remembered who it was that said it but wished to conceal her identity. "I can't remember," he replied. "I'm sure it was just a kid who had a conspiracy theory parent or crazy uncle or something like that."

"Well, there's your answer right there," Adrian said. "Don't waste your brainpower listening to conspiracy theories. And don't you keep up with any winners? I follow pretty much all of them on social media to see what they do, what they have in common, and how I can get to that level. They are all happier than us losers have ever felt at any moment in our lives. And they feel that way all the time! Arch, imagine how happy you'd be as a winner with the world at your feet and life's problems dissolved away. Wouldn't that be nice?"

"I suppose that would be nice," Archer replied.

"It would be incredible!" Adrian exclaimed.

"And look how much society has benefitted from people striving to be winners in a world without super God. Science and medicine have advanced by leaps and bounds! Human rights! Art! And it's getting exponentially better!" Adrian said as he motioned his hand toward the ceiling. "The future is bright, Arch, and human generations, one-by-one, are leading the charge to the Day!"

Archer felt defeated, even though he wasn't entirely sure that he was trying to win. "You're right, Adrian," he said. "Thanks for talking. I'm not sure what got into me."

Adrian smiled. "You know, with my PhD program's connection with the DOW, my family and friends get free HQ counseling and education. If you start to feel that way again, there's no shame in seeing a professional. It's totally anonymous, and Mom and Dad would never find out."

"I appreciate it," Archer replied. "I'll let you know if these thoughts ever come back up."

The two boys returned home and spent the rest of their vacation hanging out with their family in traditional winter break fashion. Most importantly, the Colemans celebrated Founders Day, the national holiday on the twenty-fifth of December, just as they had each year prior. "Wow, Dad. Thanks!" Archer said, opening a present on Founders Day morning. "How could you possibly have known I had my eye on the full encyclopedia set of the Great Commission with detailed descriptions of each member of the Freedom Fighters, from what I assume looks like your early childhood?" he asked sarcastically. Relations between Archer and his father had remained tense during the break.

"Those books hold a special place in my heart, Archer," Henry said. "They helped straighten out a lot of things in my life, and I felt like you could find them very useful."

Useful? Ohh, back at college. Right, he thought to himself. "Definitely. I bet they'll come in real handy," Archer finally said with a forced smile.

"All right, guys," Adrian said into his phone, "let's see what Mom and Dad got for Adrian! Hopefully it's better than that old, stinky stack of books they got Archer!"

"Hey!" Henry said.

"Shh!" Jamie said.

Adrian unwrapped his present. "New socks? New socks?" he shouted as he immediately marched toward the stairs. "Seems fair considering the present I got you was paying off your mortgage with some of my streaming money!" he shouted as he threw the package down. "But thanks for the socks!" Messages of support from his fans flooded his livestream.

"What a jerk!" Archer asked. "How were Mom and Dad supposed to know he'd do that for them?"

Henry shrugged his shoulders. "Hey, I'm not complaining."

"Oh, calm down, Archer," Jamie said. "He makes more in a week than you and I make combined in a year. He's earned the right to act however he wants."

Archer thought for a moment. "Jamie, that's not as impressive as you think it is," he replied, "considering I'm still in college, and you're on a vending machine's salary."

"Come on, you two," Nicole said. "Today's supposed to be a happy day, so no more fighting. Let's clean up the living room and head to the dining room for some breakfast. Adrian!" she yelled to her son. "I made my world-famous Founders Day flapjacks, so you better come and get 'em before we eat them all ourselves!"

Adrian opened the door to his bedroom. "You know I'm on a diet, Mom!" he screamed at the top of his lungs. "How could you shove those carbo-loaded gluten bombs in my face like that?" Adrian went back to his room and slammed the door shut behind him. More support flooded his livestream.

CHAPTER 9

Treasure Hunt

"*Au revoir*!" Jamie shouted as she and Adrian drove away.

"Goodbye! Miss you already!" Nicole shouted back.

"Boy, time really flies by when all the kids come back," Henry said.

"It sure does," Nicole replied. "When are you heading out, Archer?"

"Hmm, let's see," Archer said. "Today's Saturday, and I've got class on Monday, so I'd better head back sometime tomorrow. Ty and I are planning on meeting up for breakfast in the morning, so I'll probably leave sometime after lunch." Archer had rehearsed this speech numerous times in his head to avoid coming off as suspicious.

"Ty!" Henry exclaimed. "How's he doing? You know, I'd really like to see him myself. I think I might just tag alo—"

"No!" Archer said immediately.

Henry and Nicole were taken aback at his response.

"Ha. Ha." Archer nervously laughed. "Sorry, I just, uh, really need some bro time with Ty before I head back, that's all. We haven't been able to chat much this semester."

"Oh…okay," Henry said. "Just make sure you're back for lunch. We want to see you before you go, don't we, hun?"

"Of course!" Nicole said. "I'll always want to see my baby as long as I can."

Archer spent the rest of Saturday being lazy, in anticipation of the busy semester ahead. However, tomorrow's adventure at Franklin's farm captured his thoughts all day. He began to worry about getting caught. *If anyone asks me what I'm up to,* he thought to himself, *I'll just say I came to pay my respects to Grandpa at his headstone. But what about the shovel I'll be carrying? I'll look like a grave robber!*

Once nighttime came, Archer attempted to get some sleep, but he only managed to toss and turn for the majority of the night. Frustrated, he decided to get up, get dressed, and go downstairs.

"Good morning," Henry said as Archer walked down the stairs.

"Oh…hey, Dad. Good morning. You're up early. The sun's not even up yet!" Archer replied.

"Well, you know what they say! Early worms get the… No, wait…birds of a feather…no, wrong one."

Archer chuckled. "Well, what are you up so early for?"

"Some nights I just have trouble sleeping, and I come out here so I don't keep waking up your mother. I'm usually a good sleeper but, sometimes, my mind just gets carried away with thoughts. That's the planner in me!"

"I must have gotten that from you," Archer said. "What's your mind so worked up about?" Archer could sense from his father's non-verbal cues that something was not right.

Henry sighed. "It's your mother and I. We're going through a bit of a rough patch right now."

Archer felt his heart drop into his stomach. "I'm so sorry, Dad."

"It's okay," he said with his head hung low, not making eye contact with his son. "We'll get all our issues taken care of soon. I have no doubt about it."

Archer patted his father on the back. "That's good. You two are smart, high HQ people. I have no doubt you'll figure things out."

"Thanks, son," Henry said. "So when are you and Ty meeting up?" Henry asked.

Archer thought carefully about his response. "Nothing's set in stone, really. I might go down to Guevara's early and do some reading before Ty gets there."

"I see," Henry said. "That should be a good time! You two have been inseparable for as long as I can remember. It's hard for me to believe you guys live apart from each other now. Must be hard, huh?"

"That's just part of growing up, Dad," Archer said. "Friends become old friends, and strangers become friends in their place."

"Unfortunately you're right, son," Henry said. "Tell Ty I said hello, and I hope college has started out well for him. He's a good kid."

"I will, Dad," Archer replied. "I'm gonna get going now to make sure I can find a booth for us. I'll see you when I get back."

"All right, son. Be safe," Henry said.

Archer grabbed his backpack and began to head for the front door. He watched as his father put his head in his hands and began to cry.

"Are you okay?" Archer asked. "I can cancel on Ty and stay here with you."

Henry motioned his hand for Archer to keep going. "No, no, you should go hang out and have fun. I'll be okay. Honest."

"Uhh, okay, Dad. I'll be back soon," Archer said as he left the house. "Wow, that was unexpected," Archer said under his breath. "Can't think about that right now, though. Gotta focus on the task at hand."

Archer got in his truck and drove in the direction of the coffee shop. When he knew he was far enough away from the house, he turned around and began driving toward Franklin's old farm. In what seemed like a flash, Archer arrived. He pulled in to the gravel road that led to the barn, which was in close proximity to the pond. He parked and stepped into the barn. The sights and smells transported Archer's mind back to simpler times. He envisioned himself sitting on a hay bale, little legs swinging up and down, watching on as Franklin gathered all the supplies to go fishing. Archer could also picture the farm equipment and exactly where all his tools went, including his shovels. "Snap out of it," Archer said. "I've got a mission to complete. I can take a trip down memory lane later." Archer walked over to the area with tools hanging from the wall and grabbed an older-looking shovel. He noticed the initials "AFC" carved into the wooden handle. "I don't remember doing that," he said. "Oh well." Archer was unaware, but his grandfather had done this in anticipation of that very day.

Archer walked out of the barn and headed down toward the pond. He listened to the birds chirping as he took the familiar path leading to the water. The worries of life seemed to melt away whenever Archer visited the farm, and that day was no different. Archer approached the tree and began to dig as close to the trunk as he could. The ground was nearly frozen due to it being wintertime, so he had to put all his muscle into each thrust. He sifted through every shovelful of dirt to find his treasure. Archer repeated the dig-sift-dump process until the hole was more than three feet deep and a foot wide. The only items he found from his excavation were rocks, tree roots, and a bottle cap. Archer kept digging but was still empty-handed after an hour and a half of digging. "It's gotta be here somewhere!" he said as he continued to thrust the shovel into the hard soil.

Archer slowed down and eventually stopped for a short break to let his arms rest. After a few minutes, he persisted for another hour. *If I don't find it*, he thought to himself, sitting down against the tree, *it's all over. Everything's just been made up in my head.* Suddenly, Archer heard the sound of a twig snapping. He brought his knees into his body and leaned up close to the tree. *Someone must still live here*, he thought. *Duh! Why else would the barn have been so tidy?* Archer heard more rustling behind him and decided to speak up. "Who's there?" Archer asked. Silence. *Well I can't just sit with my back to them*, he reasoned. *I'm a sitting duck. I've gotta do something.* Archer picked up the biggest rock and held it firmly. "Now!" he said to himself as he sprang up to his feet and raised the rock above his head to strike his assailant. Two rabbits that had been grazing on the nearby grass ran away, terrified for their lives.

Archer laughed and dropped his weapon back in the dirt as the rabbits scurried into the woods. He looked at his phone to check the time. "Oh man," Archer said. "I gotta get back soon before Dad gets suspicious." He took his shovel and continued to dig furiously for another half an hour, to no avail. Archer threw down his shovel. "It's official. I'm just a crazy person! Анннннннн!" he shouted in anger.

He paced back and forth. "Dad's right! Adrian, Jamie, all my teachers—everyone was right! All that spiritual junk really is dangerous propaganda. I could have saved so much time and energy if I just listened and obeyed like everyone else! Why do I do this to myself?" he said, smacking his forehead.

After his fit of self-anger, Archer covered up the holes as best he could and put the shovel back in its rightful place in the barn. He took one more look inside. "Good riddance," he said as he slammed the door shut. In just one morning, Franklin had gone from hero to villain in Archer's mind. He was no longer a martyr for a righteous cause that opposed the oppressive powers that be. Rather Archer left thinking of his grandfather as the heinous criminal that got the punishment he deserved.

Archer started his car and drove away from the farm. Fake conversations with Ty ran through his head on the drive home so he could be prepared to answer the barrage of questions his parents were sure to ask him. Archer took one more deep breath before putting his car in park in the driveway.

"I'm back!" he shouted as he opened the front door.

"Welcome back," Henry said. "How's old Ty doing?"

Archer took off his shoes and quickly slid them out of sight as he realized mud covered the bottom of them. "He's doing really well! School's going well. The family is well. He said he's been hanging out with this girl he really likes! They're in all the same classes, and they study together, and he's really starting to have feelings for her. I'm happy for him!"

"Uh-huh," Henry said with his hands folded behind him.

He approached Archer and ran his thumb over Archer's forehead. "It looks like you've got some dirt on your forehead, Archer. Where'd that come from?"

Archer panicked internally. "Oh, uh, well…I, uh, tripped and fell on the way back to my car from the coffee shop," he quickly replied. "Ty was laughing so hard! I'm sure it was a real sight to behold. I tried getting myself cleaned up, but I must have missed a spo—"

"Stop with the lies, Archer!" Henry shouted, wiping his dirty thumb on Archer's shirt. "You're just embarrassing yourself."

Archer began to shake. "Wha—what are you talking about, Dad?"

"Oh, don't 'Dad' me," Henry said. "You know perfectly well what I'm talking about! You're lying straight through your teeth!"

Archer was at a loss for words.

"Now I've got an idea," Henry said, grabbing Archer by front of the shirt. "Why don't you have a seat on the couch over there, and we can start being a little more honest with each other."

Archer flopped onto the couch with a shove from his father.

"I know for a fact that Ty and his parents are out of town, visiting family for the weekend," Henry said. "I saw his old man at the store this week, and he mentioned it to me. There's strike one."

Archer continued to shake with fear.

"Here's strike two: I put a GPS app on your phone before you left for college. All I had to do was watch from my phone as you drove to Franklin's old farm."

Archer sank deeper into the couch.

Henry got in Archer's face. "And just what were you doing there, Archer?" Henry asked. "Would you like to finally come clean?"

Archer did not know whether to incriminate himself or double down on his lies. "I just…wanted to go there one more time and reminisce about the time I spent with Grandpa," he said, deciding on the latter. "I knew you wouldn't approve, so I had to lie."

"And lie you did," Henry replied. "Remember that vile letter I found under your bed?" he asked as he grabbed it from his pocket. "Well, I solved the little riddle he wrote for you. Take a look." Henry shoved the letter into Archer's chest.

Archer read what was written:

> "Under me we fished,
> we spoke of Roy'l visions.
> Face the 'set to find,
> Your item of admission."

"I have no idea what this means, Dad," Archer said.

A wry smile came across Henry's face. "You just don't know when to quit lying, do you? Well here's strike three: I always stood guard and watched as you two fished under that tree, so I knew immediately where he was talking about. In fact, I took a little trip to the old farm yesterday and did a little treasure hunting myself."

Archer gulped. "Did...did you find anything?" Archer asked.

"Oh I found something, all right," Henry replied.

Archer immediately sat up straight. Henry pulled out a small box originally used for holding a ring.

Archer's jaw dropped. *It is true*, he thought to himself.

"Don't you remember that the property is under constant surveillance?" Henry asked as he put the ring box on the table in front of the couch. "All I have to do is log on to my government account and watch the tapes to find out just what you were up to. How could you possibly think you were going to get away with this?"

Archer felt stupid for thinking his plan would work.

"What's even funnier," Henry said, "is that I *did* log on to my account this morning. I got to watch you digging like a madman on the direct *opposite* side of the tree! Ha!"

"But I dug everywhere on the west side," Archer said, confused. "The sun had just risen in the west, so I knew exactly where to dig."

"So you finally admit it!" Henry shouted, thrusting his index finger into Archer's chest.

Archer knew that there was no going back.

Henry continued, "And besides, the sun *sets* in the west, you imbecile."

Archer put his head in his hands.

Henry laughed. "And this whole time, I thought that you had to be smart to get into that fancy college of yours," his father remarked.

"You don't talk to my son like that!" Nicole shouted.

Henry and Archer whipped their heads around to see Nicole hopping toward them.

Archer saw that her ankles were tied together with rope.

"How'd you get out of the chair?" Henry shouted. "You're not supposed to be out here!" Henry shouted.

"A mother finds a way," Nicole said.

"Very well," Henry said. "You two leave me no choice. BOYS!" Henry clapped twice. Two men dressed in all-black suits came down the stairs.

"RUN, ARCHER!" Nicole screamed.

"But—" Archer said.

"RUNNNN!" Nicole screamed louder.

Henry attempted to grab Archer, but Archer stiff-armed his father into the couch. Without thinking, Archer grabbed the ring box and ran for the back door. The two men in suits grabbed Nicole as he was about to escape. "Come back if you ever want to see your mother again!" one of them shouted.

"Mom!" Archer exclaimed as he turned around.

"I'll be okay! We'll see each other again, I prom—" Nicole said as one of the men covered her mouth.

"I love you, Mom!" Archer shouted as he ran out the door and hopped the backyard fence.

Archer sprinted through the neighbor's yard, toward the street, and saw a familiar face sitting in a running car.

"Ty!" Archer shouted.

"GET IN! NO TIME TO EXPLAIN!" he replied.

Archer ran around to the passenger side and hopped in. "Throw you phone out or they'll be able to track us," Ty said.

Archer quickly did as he was told.

Ty threw the car in drive, stepped on the accelerator, and the two sped out of the neighborhood. Archer looked back to see if anyone was following them. He did not see any suspicious vehicles. "Don't worry," Ty said. "The two at your house have been ordered to stay with your parents. Search teams will be sent out for you shortly. We've gotta hurry."

"How can we possibly outrun the cops?" Archer asked.

"We've got our ways," Ty said.

"Who's we?"

"You'll find out."

Archer took a deep breath in and exhaled audibly. For the first time, he was able to process the events that had just transpired.

Archer worried for the safety of his mother more than anything else. Ty looked over and saw the distress on Archer's face. "The important thing is that you're safe, Arch," he said.

"Yeah," Archer replied halfheartedly. "What about my mom, though?"

"Your mom?" Ty asked. "She's a Teller?"

Archer was confused. "Like a bank teller? Come on, man, you know she's the principal," Archer replied.

Ty laughed. "No, man, a Truth Teller. Teller for short. Did the authorities grab her?"

"Yeah, they did," Archer said as his voice quivered. "I have no idea if she's a Teller, though. If she is, it was hidden perfectly well from us."

"I thought as much," Ty said.

"I've never seen her at meetings, but you never know. She might be involved, somehow, especially considering who her parents were."

Archer let these words soak in for a moment and realized the significance behind them. "You're a Transcendentalist," Archer said plainly.

"You mean the escape car didn't give that away, Sherlock?" Ty replied.

Archer laughed. "Give me a break, man. A lot's happening right now."

"Okay, okay. I guess that's fair," Ty replied. Ty continued to drive quickly through town until they had reached the city's limits. At this time, he clicked a button on the dashboard and put the pedal to the floor. The car became invisible to any onlookers.

"What did that button do?" Archer said.

"Stealth mode," Ty replied.

"Woah," Archer replied.

"Anyway, yes," Ty said. "My family and I are Transcendentalists. All my life, we've been active Truth Tellers, trying to spread the message."

"How come you never told me?" Archer asked.

"Are you kidding me?" Ty replied. "You remember that time in third grade when you told the teacher that I was, and this was your exact quote, 'spreading dangerous propaganda' at recess?"

"Hey, that's what we were taught to do when we heard something suspicious!" Archer replied. "Also propaganda is *at least* a sixth-grade-level word. I'm impressed with nine-year-old me."

"You're ridiculous," Ty said. "The point is I could never share with my best friend the deepest part of me in fear of the consequences. I wanted to tell you, believe me. I always hoped the day would come when I could openly tell you the truth. Of course, I pictured it being under less dangerous circumstances, but hey, beggars can't be choosers."

"Well," Archer said, "if nothing else, I guess all this craziness has helped cement our friendship. It hasn't been all bad."

Ty agreed. "It may not seem like it right now, but today could be the best day of your life."

"I highly doubt that," Archer said, "but what do I know anymore?"

Guuuuuurgle. "Man, I just realized I haven't eaten a thing all day," Archer said, putting his hands over his stomach. "How much longer 'til we get there?"

"We're almost to base," Ty replied.

Archer looked around at the familiar countryside surroundings. "Wait a minute," he said. "I know exactly where we're going. Is base at—"

"It is," Ty said, "I wondered how long it would take you to put two and two together."

"But they've got cameras everywhere. How can that be?"

"You'll see."

"All clear," a voice said over Ty's car speakers. Ty gripped the steering wheel with both hands as the boys approached and passed Franklin's old farm. Archer watched as a section of the road was raised up by four hydraulic arms. "Hold on, it's a little bumpy," Ty instructed as he drove the car below the raised portion of the road and slammed down onto a descending ramp, which led to a small parking lot. Ty parked the car in an empty spot.

Archer heard the hydraulics lower the road back down.

"Pretty cool, huh?" Ty asked.

Archer was motionless. "That...was...awesome!" he shouted. "This is like spy movie stuff, Ty! This whole time, I thought you were just some dorky best friend of mine, but you're out here being James freakin' Bond when no one's looking!"

"Nah, man," Ty said, laughing. "I'm just doin' my job."

"Wait," Archer said, "someone *is* looking. There are cameras all over Grandpa's place. It's under constant surveillance."

"True," Ty replied, "but the cameras only capture a defined area. Our entrance was outside of the surveillance zone."

"Genius," Archer said.

The boys got out of the car, and Archer followed Ty as he walked toward one of the walls. "I completely forgot to ask," Ty said. "By some miracle, did you happen to retrieve the package that Franklin buried for you? We watched as your father dug it up, so I know it's a long shot, but I thought I'd ask."

"You mean the ring box?" Archer said as he pulled it out of his pocket. "I completely forgot that I had it!"

"No way!" Ty exclaimed. "Take a look inside!"

Archer swung the top of the box back. "What is it?" he asked.

"It's a miniature golden yoke. Just like mine," Ty said as he held his up.

"Just like the ones in the other realm," Archer added.

"So you've been there, have you?" Ty asked. "Did you get to experience the Marketplace?"

"Did I?" Archer asked sarcastically. "I about gave away my soul in the Marketplace. Twice! Grandpa met me both times after I escaped and explained everything."

"How wonderful!" Ty exclaimed. "And you visited the King, I assume?" Ty bowed. Ty observed that Archer did not bow at the name of the King. "I see," Ty said. "We'll arrange that later, if you want."

"Potentially," Archer said. Archer began to inspect the miniature golden yoke from the ring box. "Hey, Ty," he said. "What does the inscription on the back mean? It says: 'Archer, Be a Noble Horse. Love, Grandpa.'"

"I'll show you," Ty said as he knocked on the wall in a secret pattern. Up, down, left, right, center, up, down, left, right, center. Ty completed the sequence and stepped back as a small compartment jutted out from the wall. He opened the lid. "Place it here, Archer."

Archer looked inside and saw an indention the size of the yoke. He placed the golden yoke inside.

"Rotate it 180 degrees," Ty instructed.

Archer did as he was told.

"What is your purpose?" a voice said from the speaker on the compartment.

Archer shrugged his shoulders. "What am I supposed to say?"

"Try what was written on the yoke," he replied.

Archer leaned close to the speaker. "Be a Noble Horse?"

"Very well," the voice said. The lid lowered, and the compartment slid back into the wall. *Click.* Suddenly a door jutted out from the wall. Ty slid it to the side, revealing a hallway.

"Welcome, Archer," two people said simultaneously. "We're happy to see you."

Archer immediately recognized the voices to be from Ty's parents, Sasha and Aaron.

"Oh my gosh!" Archer said as he hugged them. "You don't know how good it is to see some friendly faces!"

"Did you escape without harm?" Sasha asked as she investigated his arms for cuts or bruises.

"Yes," Archer said. "I got out before the two men in black suits could get ahold of me."

"Good," Aaron said.

"But what about my mom?" Archer asked. "They told me I'd never see her again if I left." Archer's eyes welled up.

"We'll do our best to make sure that you and her reunite as quickly as possible," Sasha said, patting Archer on the back. "Now let's show you around the place and give you a taste of what we do here."

Archer was led through a small hallway to an open room buzzing with activity. Around the perimeter of the central room were conference rooms. "This," Aaron said, "is Truth Teller headquarters."

Archer was awestruck with the size of the operation. "You mean to tell me that all of this was right beneath my feet every time I was at Grandpa's?"

"Indeed," Aaron said. "In fact, we had more members working here during Franklin's lifetime."

Archer looked around and saw members speaking into their headsets and typing at their computers. "Why is it here?" Archer asked.

"Originally, the Truth Tellers were located in Capital City," Aaron explained. "Over time, the city became too dangerous of a place to conduct our affairs. The elders decided to put the new headquarters in a safer location once our first leader passed away, as she was advancing in age by that point. Before she died, she declared that Franklin was to be her successor and that he should choose where it was built. Unfortunately Franklin was captured and exiled to this location before that decision was to be made, which forced our hand a bit. The funny thing is that we couldn't have selected a better location ourselves. The distance away from any major population centers allows us to operate secretly with relative ease. So the authorities ended up aiding us. What they intended for punishment worked out for our overall good."

"Talk about a backfire," Archer said.

"Evil plans never prosper, Archer." Sasha said. "Remember that."

Aaron continued, "Communication with Franklin was tough, but we are a smart and determined group. Construction crews built elaborate tunnels starting from outside the surveillance zone to beneath Franklin's house, where they built the offices you see here. Eventually they constructed an elevator system leading directly underneath Franklin's bed. They installed a trapdoor underneath it and provided Franklin with a life-sized mannequin he would carefully put in his place every night. Franklin would then drop through the hatch under his bed, ride the elevator, and begin work for the night."

"So you built it here because Grandpa couldn't leave or communicate with the outside world?" Archer asked.

"Correct," Aaron replied. "We had to have it here, otherwise Franklin wouldn't have been able to continue leading the mission."

"And what all do you do here?" Archer asked.

"Here at headquarters, we manage all of the logistics for Teller activity worldwide," Sasha replied. "One of our main responsibilities is organizing the safe transportation of wanted individuals, such as yourself, by trained escape specialists, such as Ty."

Ty waved at Archer.

"We originally voted against sending Ty to work your case, as he had just completed his training a week prior," Sasha continued. "In addition, yours was a particularly dangerous escape. However, we knew that he had what it took and that he would do whatever it took to help his friend."

Ty nodded and smiled at Archer.

"Thank you, Ty," Archer said. "I never imagined I'd have a friend willing to risk their life for me."

"No thanks necessary," Ty replied. "That's what people do when they've had the same done for them."

Archer and Ty did their secret handshake.

"Most importantly," Sasha continued, "we provide education to individuals who wish to learn more about the Transcendent realm and the kingdom. In essence, as our name implies, we tell the Truth."

"Amazing," Archer said.

Ty and his parents escorted Archer around the main operational room. Archer observed the workers as they conducted their daily affairs. Archer stopped to watch a video interview on one of their computer screens. "This is just incredible," he said. "They're talking to people from all around the world! Look at that! China, Russia, France, Argentina, Somalia, Iran—"

Upon hearing Archer's voice, one of the workers turned around. "I thought that was your voice!" she exclaimed.

"Grace?" Archer said as he nearly fainted at the sight of her.

"Oh I'm so glad that you're okay!" she said, hugging him.

"You work here too?" Archer asked.

"I sure do," she replied proudly. "Oh I'm so glad you were able to get here safely."

"Let's give these two some privacy," Sasha said, smiling. "I'm sure they have a lot to catch up on."

"Actually," Grace replied, "I've still got a lot of work to do with the Hernandez case in Mexico. Archer and I can chat later. Just let me get back to—"

"I can take over for you," Ty said, sitting down in her chair. "It is long past the time for you two to go on a date with each other."

Archer and Grace's faces began to blush.

"Oh come on," Ty said. "You're really gonna act like I don't know what's going on between you two? Alllllll day at school, I'd listen to Arch talk about Grace this and Grace that, blah, blah, blah. And then whenever Grace and I shared a shift here, I'd sit allllll night and listen to her talk about Archer and how cute he is, how funny he is, blah, blah, blah."

Archer and Grace laughed.

"You really think I'm cute?" Archer asked Grace, flexing his biceps and striking a pose.

"Not so much when you do that," she said, laughing. "But otherwise...yeah."

Archer blushed even more.

"You two crazy kids get out of here and go have fun," Ty said. "We've set up a nice candlelit dinner in conference room 12."

"Wow, thanks, Ty," Archer said, slapping Ty on the shoulder. "You officially win 'wingman of the year' award."

"Get out of here already!" Ty said, putting on his headset.

Grace wrapped her arms around Ty's neck and hugged him.

"All right, lead the way," Archer said to Grace.

Grace extended her hand toward Archer, and the two walked hand-in-hand to conference room 12.

Awaiting them was a room containing one small table with a white tablecloth draped over it. On the table were two spaghetti dinners and a large red candle lit in the center. Archer pulled out her chair, and Grace took a seat. "Thank you, kind sir," she said.

Archer sat down opposite her.

The two of them smiled at each other.

"We finally did it," Archer said.

"Did what?" Grace said.

"Don't play coy," Archer said. "You know we've been playing this touch-and-go, hard-to-get game since we were little kids."

"What?" Grace replied. "No way! I sent you so many signals to ask me out on a date!"

"You did?" Archer said.

"Yes! I pretty much did everything but buy a billboard," Grace said. "I was really sad you didn't text me after I talked to you on the first day of our senior year. I had to work up a lot of courage to do that, you know!"

"Really?" he said. "Well I really wanted to ask you out! Honest, I did. I was just scared that you didn't like me like that, and I would just make it awkward between us."

"You want to talk about awkward?" Grace asked. "What about the times throughout the years you never texted me back? That made it pretty awkward, didn't it? *And* you forgot our plan to meet up before we left for college. That was no picnic to deal with either! *And! And!* You never tried to contact me once while we were both at the same stinking college! What the heck?"

"Yikes, my bad," Archer replied. "But you could have just asked me out on a date directly. That would have been great!"

Grace looked at him sternly. "Hey, mister, you gotta put a little bit of effort into this thing, too."

"Okay, okay, you're right. I dropped the ball. But hey, all's well that ends well, right?" he said, raising his eyebrows up and down.

"I guess," she said, smiling.

Archer put a napkin on his lap and rubbed his hands together. "Boy, does this look good," he said. "Let's dig in." Archer started eating. He saw that Grace had closed her eyes and was not eating. "What are you doing?" Archer asked.

Grace opened her eyes and put a napkin on her lap. "I was giving thanks for the food," she replied.

Archer looked around the room. "Telepathically? To whom?" he asked.

Grace laughed. "You know what? In a way, I guess it kind of is telepathic."

She twirled noodles around her fork and took a bite. "We give thanks to the King"—she bowed her head—"because it's through Him that we're able to enjoy all things, especially food. We like to show our gratitude for our meals and remember that our earthly food is a symbol for the eternal food that our soul needs for its nourishment."

Archer continued to scarf down his meal. "I see," he said with a mouthful of spaghetti.

"I can't imagine how strange all this probably sounds to someone who wasn't taught it growing up," she said. "We talk to nonbelievers all the time and help share the message with them, but it's difficult for me to fully understand where they're coming from. I'd really like to have those types of conversations with you."

"I'd like that too," Archer replied, just before taking a bite of his garlic bread. "I bet growing up with all these secrets was tough too."

"It was," Grace replied. "It's especially tough when you're young. As a kid, you can't fully understand the dangers of talking about non-approved topics. So parents are conflicted. On the one hand, they want to teach their children the Truth because they think that's what good parents do. On the other hand, kids are blabbermouths and don't know when to be quiet. The authorities use this to their advantage. Countless families have been torn apart as a result of children telling the wrong people what they have seen and heard at home."

"Dang," Archer said. "That's pretty messed up."

"It's very sad to see," Grace replied. "My parents ultimately decided to teach my siblings and I the Truth from the very beginning," Grace said. "We were basically raised down here. These people are my second family. I was fortunate to have such incredible resources at my fingertips from day one. Like that older gentleman in the red sweater over there, do you see him?"

Archer looked through the front glass wall and saw the man. "I see him."

"His name is Tony," she said. "He specializes in educating children in the tactics that authorities use to trick them into confessing secrets. I learned a lot from him. Remember the one-on-one coun-selor/student meetings we would have, every once in a while, in elementary school?"

"Oh yeah," Archer answered. "I remember those. It was always so much fun hearing your name called and having a free pass to get out of class. They always had my favorite candies too!"

"Well I'm glad one of us enjoyed them," Grace replied. "Those were actually assigned intel officers, seeking to gain information on the Truth Tellers from unsuspecting children. I was always so worried on the walk to the counselor's office that I would accidentally get somebody in trouble. Thankfully, Tony trained me well on how to answer the questions inconspicuously."

"Wow," Archer said. "Here I was, just some happy-go-lucky kid playing on the playground with my friends and learning how to add and subtract, while you're out there worried about saying one wrong word and getting your parents taken away."

"It's difficult, no doubt," Grace said. "But we believe that children like you are in much graver danger than I ever was."

"Like the spiritual danger?" Archer asked.

"Exactly. Eternal danger," she replied. "I can't tell you how many nights I stayed up asking Him to deliver you from the evil one. There were so many times I doubted Him and became angry because it seemed like He wasn't answering me."

"You really did that for me?" Archer asked.

Grace nodded her head up and down.

"You're the best," Archer replied.

Grace smiled.

"So how did you combat those feelings of doubt and anger toward Him?" Archer asked.

"It was tough, but I had to remind myself over and over of the Truths that I had been taught. Have you been taught any of the Truths yet, Archer?"

"No, I have no idea what you're talking about."

"Hold tight," Grace said as she walked out of the room. She came back with a laminated sheet and placed it in front of Archer.

"We have these posted all over the walls as a constant reminder. You can keep this one."

Archer read the sheet:

Eternal Truths:

1) He loves you no matter what.
2) He desires eternal prosperity for you.
3) He died for you so that you may have citizenship in His kingdom.

Archer read these Truths over and over.

"Is that a good silence or more of a confused one?" Grace asked, hoping it was the former.

"I don't know yet," Archer replied.

"That is totally fine!" Grace said reassuringly. "Like I said, this all has to be so strange to hear for the first time, so take as much time as you need."

"To be honest," Archer said, "this isn't the first time I've heard about this. Except for number three. I've never heard that part."

Grace's eyes lit up. "Who told you about the Transcendent realm?" she asked. "Because we know for a fact that your grandpa didn't teach you. We were able to hack the security cameras and microphones on Franklin's property and transcribe every conversation you two ever had. I read over them all, and there was never a direct mention of the kingdom."

"Woah, that's kinda creepy," Archer said jokingly. "Can I read them sometime?"

"Sure!" Grace replied.

"Well, he may not have told me then," Archer said, "but Grandpa has told me about the kingdom and a little bit about what the King is like."

Grace bowed. "Like in the other realm?" she asked, realizing what he meant.

"Yep," Archer said. "The past couple years, I've gone there randomly and met with Grandpa."

"That's amazing, Archer!" Grace said. "Have you entered the kingdom and met Him yet?"

"No," he said in an ashamed tone. "I came close, but I didn't get past the gate."

"No, no, no," she quickly replied, "there's no shame in that! It obviously wasn't the right time for you. Just know that the gates are always open whenever you want to come to Him."

Archer felt comforted.

"Besides," Grace added, "I used to visit the other realm often, and it wasn't until after a few trips that I met Him."

"But I thought you said that your parents taught you about Him from an early age?" Archer asked. "Why didn't you just go see Him the first time?"

"Fair question," Grace replied, "but just because I was taught it didn't mean I had taken the message to heart. Some people, like me, are lucky to be born inside the walls of the kingdom because that's where their parents reside. This is great, but at a certain age, the child grows up and begins to understand what right and wrong are. They understand how to choose to do wrong. At this point, the responsibility is on the person to choose if they want to meet the King and accept the golden yoke or if they're going to leave the kingdom and take up another yoke." Grace bowed. "It's a completely personal decision, and He wants us to make it on our own."

"I guess that makes sense," Archer said. "When can I go back and see Him?"

"You can go back whenever you're ready," Grace replied. She continued, "What's interesting about humans is that we are most ready to give our hearts to Him at two opposite times: when we're on top of the mountain and everything is going perfectly or when we're in the lowest valleys of our lives. It differs for every person, but more often than not, it's the suffering in the valleys that catalyzes our desire for Him."

Archer took his final bite of spaghetti.

"Think back to what was going on in your life when you visited the other realm," Grace instructed. "Were things going well or not so well in your life?"

"Well," Archer said, "the first time I went was after a big fight with my sister, Jamie, so I guess not so well. And the second time was the night that I got accepted into Helmuth, which was a really good day. The third time was…hmm…what was I doing? Oh yeah! That was the day I skipped classes in college and stayed in my dorm all day. That last one seems a little random, doesn't it?"

"Maybe on the surface," Grace said. "Let's dig a little deeper on all three."

Archer wiped his mouth with the napkin and threw it on the plate.

"The first visit sounds like one of those lows that I was talking about. Fighting with family is really hard on a person, especially if we look up to them."

"Yeah, I suppose," Archer replied. "Plus I'm pretty sure I'd had a bad day at school. It was all-around a bad day. What about the other two?"

Grace thought for a few moments. "Well I'm no expert by any means, but the second visit could have been one of those times where He felt that you were falling into a trap that the enemy had set for you. Even I could see your head getting bigger by the social media post!"

"Enemy?" Archer asked. "As in Antipalos?"

Grace cringed at the sound of his name. "I see you've become acquainted with him," she said. "I'm not surprised, though. Most people meet him before they meet His Highness. Yes, he is the enemy," she said. "Antipalos seeks your destruction. He hates you, Archer."

"Why me?" Archer asked.

"Antipalos hates you because he hates Him," Grace replied. "You resemble His Highness, and His Highness is the very essence of love. You were designed to love like He does. And Antipalos *hates* love. He's too weak to take on more than one person at a time, so he hates anything that connects people because then he can't control them. Therefore, Antipalos hates His Highness, he hates love, and he hates you."

"You lost me there," Archer said. "How can the King be the essence of love? That's just an emotion."

Grace bowed her head. "Let me put it this way, and maybe it'll help," she replied. "Antipalos is weak and a coward. He knows the only way he can capture people is by isolating them. He's only strong enough to capture one detached person at a time. His Highness, on the other hand, can hold us in His arms all together, all at once. Still tracking?"

"I think so," Archer said.

"Great," she said. "Now ask yourself: which type of person is more likely to end up alone, depressed, and angry? A prideful, greedy, jealous person? Or a selfless, giving, peaceful person?"

Archer put his index finger over his mouth and thought through the question. "It's gotta be the first one," he answered. "Who wants to be around a person like that?"

"Exactly!" Grace said. "That's the strategy the enemy uses against us. He tries to trick us into thinking that our pursuit of success will lead to a happy life. So in your case, I believe His Highness sensed that you were falling hard for this trap and that you could benefit greatly from a trip to the spiritual realm."

"Correct me if I'm wrong," Archer said, "but that sounds like the HQ system in a nutshell. Does it not?"

"*Ding! Ding! Ding!* You nailed it!" Grace said. "The whole system is built on pride, greed, and jealousy that's cleverly disguised as ambition. Think back to my earlier question. You said a prideful, greedy, jealous person would end up alone, depressed, and angry. That's the type of person that the self-centered HQ system produces. The perfect person for the enemy to capture."

Archer had a hard time comprehending the negatives of the HQ system after a lifetime of conditioning to worship it. However, he knew what Grace was saying was correct because that's exactly what he experienced. His pursuit of a higher HQ score always left him feeling increasingly isolated and lonely. "I remember now what I had done the day of my third visit," Archer finally said, breaking the silence.

Grace looked at Archer and nodded, indicating that she was ready to listen.

"I had finally given my heart to a life of HQ that day," Archer said. "I *completely* believed it was the path to happiness. Professor Espinoza was so convincing in his lecture."

"It's really common for kids our age to say things like that," Grace said. "You're a common case."

"I don't doubt it. It was so easy to believe him," Archer said. "So, for the rest of the day, I sat at my laptop, researching tips and tricks to increase my score so one day I could become a winner."

"I see," Grace said. "Do you see now why that may have been a good time to be transported to the other realm?"

"Totally," Archer replied. "I was like a bear with my leg caught in the trap. The hunter was on his way to come and take me away. Thankfully I found myself back in the other realm where I was able to look Antipalos directly in his cold, dead eyes for myself and run away. There's no way I would have been able to see the deceitfulness of it all, if I hadn't been there. Now I know why Grandpa said I should be upset if I couldn't go to the other realm anymore."

"Wow," Grace said. "what an amazing experience. Not many people have actually looked Antipalos in his eyes and escaped his clutches. He must *really* be out for you now."

"Bring it on," Archer replied confidently.

Archer looked at the Eternal Truths sheet again. "So what does number three mean? When did He die for me?" he asked.

Grace looked deeply into Archer's eyes. "Archer," she said, "I think you're ready to go meet Him and have Him explain it to you face-to-face."

"You know what?" Archer replied. "I am ready. How can I do that?"

Grace stood up and opened the door. "Right this way." Grace led Archer back into the main lobby where they walked directly to a room on the opposite wall. Archer read the nameplate beside the room: Prayer Room. Grace opened the door, and the two entered. The walls were decorated with natural scenes, and the room contained many plants and a small, operating waterfall.

"The prayer room is a quiet place designed to help keep out distractions and calm down our spirits," Grace said as she led him inside. "Although we can talk to His Highness anywhere and at any time, most people enjoy the calming effect of nature, so we've recreated it in here. Here, lie down on this couch."

Archer walked over and did as he was told.

"Great. Now slowly close your eyes and become aware of your breathing." Archer folded his hands across his chest and closed his eyes.

"Perfect," Grace said. "Now what I want you to do is to have a conversation with His Highness like you were just having with me."

"Okay?" Archer replied. "And how am I supposed to start it? 'Howdy, partner?' That doesn't feel right."

Grace laughed. "Any way you want, Archer. Whether out loud or internally, He'll respond if you listen."

Archer took a deep breath. "Hi, Your Highness," he said aloud. "It's Archer Coleman. I just wanted to say hi, I guess, and, uhh, meet you for the first time. I've heard a lot about you from people I trust, and I think I've reached a point where I want to experience you for myself. So, uhh, yeah…sincerely, Archer? I don't really know how to end it." Archer laid on the couch with his eyes closed, waiting for a response. He continued to lay there silently. "I don't hear anything, Grace," he said, eventually. "I don't think it's working."

"Look around, Archer. It did work."

Archer opened his eyes and sat up.

"Salutations, Archer. It's good to see you again," Franklin said.

"Hi, Grandpa. It's good to see you too," Archer replied, rubbing his eyes.

"Do you recognize where you're at?" Franklin asked.

Archer looked at his surroundings. "Uhh, sort of. Is this the sidewalk north of the Marketplace?"

"Precisely," Franklin said. "Archer, this is the exact spot where you decided to stop journeying toward the kingdom's gate the first time."

Archer was stunned. "There's no way I was this far away! I about burned alive last time! Surely I was closer than here. The gate looks like it's at least a half mile away," Archer said, squinting his eyes to try and bring it into focus.

"It's true, Archer. I was with you," Franklin replied. "The power radiating from His Highness is dangerous to those who don't have a healthy way to receive it. You were much farther away than previously thought."

Archer still couldn't believe it. "Well, I feel fine right now. Should we start walking that way?" Archer said.

"Lead the way," Franklin insisted. "I'm very glad your friends were able to save you from the authorities," Franklin said as they began walking toward the kingdom. "I always prayed that none of my family would have to go through what I went through."

"Me too," Archer replied. "Although I think I'm worried about Mom. Do you know if they took her?"

Franklin sighed. "Yes," he said. "They took Nicole to a reeducation camp. Your father made sure of it."

Archer's face immediately turned red, and he burned with anger toward his father. Archer kicked over the nearest trash can and screamed.

"Archer! Archer! Calm down," Franklin said. "It'll be okay. Nicole will be fine."

Archer stood with his hands interlocked on the top of his head, still breathing heavily.

"You're going to have to forgive your father if you wish to enter the kingdom," Franklin said.

"What? Why?" Archer asked. "He wronged me. He wronged the family. I just want him punished for hurting me and my mom, and I don't think that's such a bad thing to want."

Franklin nodded. "Yes, justice is a desire put on all our hearts. But we were not created to be the judges. Only His Highness is able to judge absolutely, objectively." Franklin put his arm around Archer's shoulder. "Let's sit on this bench over here, and I'll tell you the story of why you must forgive to enter the kingdom's gates."

Archer and Franklin sat down on the bench.

An older and a younger woman passed them on the sidewalk. "Hello, Franklin," the older woman said. "Is this your kin?"

"Hi, Martha," Franklin answered. "It sure is. This is my grand-son, Archer. He says he wants to meet the King today."

Franklin and Martha bowed.

"Oh how wonderful!" she exclaimed. "Well, congratulations, Mr. Archer, and welcome to the family. My granddaughter, Michelle, here has also decided to meet His Highness today. You two will have the same birthday!"

Archer looked at his grandfather with a confused expression.

"When you enter the kingdom for the first time, it's like your birthday there. You'll understand it later," Franklin whispered.

"Well, I don't want to hold you two up any longer! It was good seeing you, Franklin!"

"You too, Martha," Franklin said. "Congratulations, Michelle!"

The two women strolled away in the direction of the kingdom.

"Now where were we?" Franklin asked.

"Forgiveness," Archer said, still upset at his father.

"Ahh, yes. Forgiveness," Franklin said. "Have you ever won-dered what the Freedom Fighters freed the people *from*, Archer?"

"Of course," Archer replied. "It was from old, rigid, bigoted ways of thinking. They freed people to use their time and energy to think about more useful things."

"No," Franklin said. "It's deeper than that. There was a time when great numbers of people's souls already experienced freedom. They lived freely in the kingdom with Him. These people lived a life full of peace, meaning, and fulfillment, no matter what earthly chal-lenges were thrown at them. They experienced *real, enduring* free-dom. But there was widespread rebellion against the King because many people were deceived into thinking that living under the King's laws was rigid and bigoted, as you say. Scores of people denounced their citizenship and forfeited the freedom that He offered. Antipalos was the driving force behind this rebellion, as you may have guessed."

"I had a hunch," Archer said.

Franklin continued, "Antipalos was originally a high-ranking official of the royal military that served in the King's palace. Day in and day out, he watched enviously as His Highness ruled over His creation."

"Timeout," Archer said. "What do you mean by creation?"

"What I mean is, His Highness built everything in the kingdom," Franklin replied. "He even built you and me."

Archer shook his head in disbelief. "Okay, that's just crazy talk, Grandpa. You expect me to believe that He can build a human?"

"That's exactly what I want you to believe, Archer, because it's the Truth," Franklin replied. "In the beginning, His Highness created the kingdom and everything in it. Every single one of the elements and compounds that make up living and nonliving materials were His creation. He even created special kingdom helpers, which included the military and its warriors, including Antipalos. It was all good in His eyes, but there was one major piece missing. He desired to share his unconditional love with higher, sentient beings whose purpose was to take care of the earth and live in eternal happiness with Him. So he created the human."

Archer remained skeptical.

Franklin continued, "Long before humans entered the fold, Antipalos' self-centered lust for power became unbearable to the point where he attempted a coup to overthrow His Highness. Antipalos recruited many of his military colleagues to fight in this civil war. The royal army prevailed against the rebels, and His Highness had no choice but to dispel them all from the kingdom. This was the first time anyone had ever left the kingdom's walls.

"Antipalos' lust for power and hatred of the King has only grown since his banishment." Franklin bowed. "The coward now realizes that he can never be strong enough to overthrow His Highness and rule over the original kingdom, so his new strategy is to convince the kingdom's citizens to deny their citizenship and refuse to pledge their allegiance to His Highness. In this way, they enter his domain and become his very own subjects."

"How does he do that?" Archer asked.

"The gates of the kingdom are not permitted to be shut," Franklin replied, "so Antipalos is able to shout these lies and false promises directly to those inside who find themselves close to the gate.

"So the first rebellious humans denounced their citizenship and exited through the open gate and found only the vast, desolate lands of the Transcendent realm. Antipalos smartly smuggled food and building material outside the kingdom so they would not need to go running back inside. Eventually this led to the building of everything outside of the kingdom, including the Marketplace, with its temples to false kings."

"I see," Archer said, remembering all the buildings and flashing lights. "What convinced those early people to leave the kingdom?" Archer asked.

"Good question," Franklin replied. "For the most part, ancient peoples still believed that they should worship things bigger than themselves, usually as part of their group's identity. Some civilizations worshipped an animal, some worshipped another human, and others worshipped mythical gods. At that time, Antipalos' mission was to make sure they worshipped anything other than His Highness. This was the norm for thousands of earthly years, leading up to our modern day."

"What's it like now?" Archer asked.

Franklin paused to articulate his words carefully. "Antipalos began to use the human race's intellectual and social advancements against itself," he said. "This new age environment lent itself well to the lie that individuals should be the center of their own universe to experience true happiness. He bellowed out that the kingdom is oppressive and that the King opposes their happiness, which, Antipalos cleverly stated, was the new meaning of life. 'Why would He restrict your deepest desires and feelings if He really loved you? Didn't He create you that way? Can't you see that He is ruling you with an iron fist in a velvet glove?' Modern people are more likely to believe these lies and leave the kingdom, thinking they have freed themselves from all forms of laws and boundaries. *True freedom*, they tell themselves. Antipalos happily greets them at the gate with a welcome basket filled with construction material. 'Build up your kingdom and live in it!' Antipalos instructs them. 'Become the ruler, the lawmaker, and the judge of your life. Only you have the right to decide the way you should live.'

"So instead of many people building and worshipping at one mighty altar, as was done in ancient times, modern peoples leave the kingdom and go straight to building a kingdom-of-one with an altar dedicated to themselves. And this, Archer, is precisely what Antipalos desires. He's quite cunning in that way. Cowardly? Yes. Weak? Immeasurably. But he knows his limits, and he knows that he can more easily control smaller kingdoms."

"Makes sense," Archer said. "So, for example, that guy in the Marketplace whose heart was overtaken by money, you're saying that money was the false god that he pledged his allegiance to?"

"Yes and no," Franklin replied. "Had you looked deeper into that man's soul, you would have seen his ultimate allegiance: himself. When it comes down to it, the question is: do you choose to worship the King or do you choose to worship yourself?" Franklin bowed.

"It's got to be more complicated than that," Archer insisted.

"It really isn't," Franklin replied. "It's as simple as that."

He continued, "Those buildings in the Marketplace represent ways in which humans experience their feelings of self-importance and self-worth. They're means to an end. It does not matter if a person chooses to dedicate their life to a so-called virtue, to an evil vice, or anything in-between. People leave those buildings and take roads that always lead back to their own little kingdom or queendom of one. And, unfortunately, a life lived for the self always ends in tragedy.

"Over time, more solitary kingdoms and queendoms were built, and more children were born outside of the kingdom. In fact, the population outside has so greatly increased that some children are born at a mighty distance away and are thus unable to see the kingdom. The enemy delights in this situation because he is able to fill their heads with the ultimate lie that the kingdom does not even exist. In fact, Antipalos is even willing to say that *he himself* does not exist. This has proved a much easier task than teaching people that see the kingdom to avoid it at all costs."

"Genius," Archer said.

"Unfortunately so," Franklin said. "We are designed to orbit around His Highness, like planets around a star. This is the only way to have complete meaning and fulfillment in life. However, modern society has chosen to flip the script. Rather than all the planets harmoniously orbiting around the sun and receiving the life energy that it provides, each planet now demands every other object to orbit around it.

"Add all of this up, Franklin said, "and we can view our modern-day circumstance: a society of people who believe solely in a physical realm where humans find fulfillment through individual achievement and self-realization—a guaranteed pathway to disorganization and isolation of the highest order." Franklin hung his head low.

"Wow," Archer said. "That seems like a dead-end way to live life. I know myself, and I mess up on a daily basis. Placing my happiness and fulfillment on my own shoulders would just crush me. I may do good one day, but I can't be perfect all the time. I'm setting myself up for failure."

"You're wise beyond your years, Archer," Franklin replied.

"So how are citizens of the kingdom supposed to accept people that live outside it?" Archer asked. "Insiders must surely view those people like the enemies. I mean, that's what religion teaches, right?"

"*Incorrect religious teaching* declares that other humans are the enemy," Franklin replied. "Antipalos is the true enemy. Those outside the kingdom are still our brothers and sisters. They have just been deceived. His Highness instructs us to love them and view them as lost brothers and sisters of the kingdom."

"Hold up," Archer said. "That sounds nice and all, but it's gotta be impossible not to look down on them. Insiders are the 'good' people and outsiders are the 'bad' people."

"This is where we arrive at the topic of forgiveness," Franklin replied. "You mentioned before that you know deep down when you mess up, right?" Franklin asked.

"Yeah, I remember saying that," Archer replied.

"Well, what if I told you that everyone has messed up a time or two in life. Would you believe me?" Archer laughed.

"Of course I would. No one's perfect."

"Exactly right," Franklin replied. "In light of that, consider this: His Highness decreed that all those mess ups be judged and penalized before entering his kingdom. No one is allowed inside until every single mess up on their personal record has been punished.

"But if everyone has messed up," Archer said, "and no one is allowed inside that has mess ups on their permanent record, how can anyone be allowed to enter?"

"You twisted my words," Franklin replied, "Those who have messed up *are* allowed to enter. It's just that their mess ups bring about fines, and all those fines must be paid before entrance. Do you see now?"

Archer thought for a moment. "So how do you pay the fines?"

"You can't," Franklin said, smiling.

"Okay, now I know you're just playing with me," Archer said.

"I'm not!" Franklin replied. "Humans weren't created with the ability to pay their fines. That fine is on your record forever *unless* you ask His Highness to pay it for you."

"So all I have to do to enter the kingdom is to ask Him to pay my fines for me."

"In a way, but it's a little deeper than that," Franklin replied. "His Majesty always knew humans would take advantage of the free will He bestowed unto them at their creation and leave the kingdom. This free will, which is the *choice* to live inside or outside the kingdom, is necessary for true love. He desired for humans to experience the true love and happiness that He experiences. In fact, He not only experiences them, but He is also where all good things come from. He wants to give humans that experience of true love in his perfect kingdom for eternity."

"I think I get it," Archer said. "Forcing someone to love isn't true love. It's a big risk, but He wanted to offer a big reward."

"Exactly!" Franklin exclaimed. "Imagine if a wife is forced to stay with her husband, no matter what. Would you call that true love? I wouldn't."

"I wouldn't either," Archer said. "I'd say it's not fair for her."

"Precisely. Now here's the cool part," Franklin continued. "He knew that imperfect humans could not enter back into His perfect kingdom without paying their fines on their record, like I mentioned."

"Wait, I know this one too!" Archer interrupted.

"Go on," Franklin replied.

"This is where He just forgave everyone and cleaned off their record! He's the source of all good things, and forgiveness is a really good thing, right?"

"You're on the right track but not quite," Franklin replied. "You see, He refuses to forgive me or you, just for the sake of forgiveness."

"That's doesn't seem fair," Archer said.

"Quite the contrary, Archer!" Franklin exclaimed. "He won't do that because He's *completely* fair. He vowed, long ago, to punish all wrongdoing fairly. Every victim would be allowed to have their case heard in court. His Highness despises when someone is harmed, and He detests when that mistreatment goes unpunished.

"This brings us to the crux of the issue. Every human of discerning age will abuse their free will and be unfit to enter the kingdom. How, then, is a mortal human supposed to pay for a spiritual crime, clean themselves up, and enter the kingdom? Can they unsay the mean words they said? Can they unabuse the person they hurt? Of course not. So He had a choice. Was He going to go back on His word and allow crime to go unpunished and victims to be left without justice? Or was He only going to allow perfect humans into the kingdom? Both of those options were unsatisfactory to Him. Evil needs to be punished, and He longs for eternal relationship with His creation. The solution He came to was this: He would leave the kingdom and pay for humanity's crimes Himself. He loves His creation too much to sit idly by as they're shut out of the kingdom forever with no path back inside."

"His Highness is able to leave the kingdom?" Archer asked, perplexed by the thought.

"Indeed," Franklin replied. "He is the creator of all things, even things and people that left the kingdom and are now here in the enemy's territory."

Archer was still struggling with the concept.

"This is a complicated topic, Archer," Franklin said. "Don't try and understand all the details at once. You have a long life ahead of you to learn and grow. As I mentioned before," Franklin said, "He is where all good things begin. And evil, it turns out, is just the absence of good. Similarly darkness is not a thing in and of itself. It is the absence of light, just as loneliness is the absence of relationship. Therefore, fair punishment for evil is subjecting the criminal to the equal amount of evil, which is the absence of good that they withheld from their victims. Humans figured this out long ago. Criminals are locked up in prison, which is the absence of freedom. Taken to the extreme, the absence of life is death, and some criminals get the death sentence."

"That's an interesting way to look at things," Archer said. "But that seems kind of unrelated. Where's all this leading?"

"It's leading to the greatest act of love ever performed," Franklin replied. "*Not only* did His Majesty leave His high position in the kingdom, He chose to become a lowly human just like us," Franklin said. "By doing this, He could go to court and stand there as a human while the judge read Him every one of humanity's crimes and the accompanying punishment for those crimes. He chose to endure the punishment you and I and everyone else deserve so that we could enter the kingdom and live with Him again."

"Ultimately," Franklin continued, "the fair punishment deserved for all the evil that humanity has committed was to have evil done to them in return. In other words, humans deserved to be separated from experiencing anything that is good, but He took that punishment instead. Just like a person with all the money in the world is only able to fully pay back a fine that is worth all the money in the world, a perfect human that committed no crimes is the only one that can completely serve the punishment for all crimes ever committed. And that ultimate punishment was the absence of good, absence of light, and absence of relationship, also known as absolute evil, darkness, and loneliness."

Archer began to tear up.

"So he demoted himself to becoming human because He was to stand *in the place of humans*. Justice would not have been fully paid back had He experienced these punishments as a King. Think about it, Archer!" Franklin said. "His Highness left the kingdom, where He had full and total authority, to enter the enemy's territory, where the enemy was allowed to have temporary authority."

"That is hard to imagine giving up that much power for someone else," Archer replied. "How did Antipalos react to that?"

"He delighted in the opportunity," Franklin replied. "'Finally!' he shouted upon seeing Him in human form. 'I am now more powerful than He! Now is my chance to strike a death blow and overtake the kingdom!' So, as His Highness lived His earthly life, Antipalos convinced many to hate Him. He made sure that His Highness was captured, sent to a kangaroo court, and was sentenced to die for no personal crime of His own. Antipalos used his strongest weapon to defeat His Highness: death itself. However, unbeknownst to him, Antipalos was helping His Highness accomplish His goal of providing a path for humans back into the kingdom.

"So, when the time had come, His Highness was tortured and killed in utter loneliness. His friends deserted Him, and He denied His identity as Himself, a King, which could have saved Him from this grisly, earthly death. 'I won!' the enemy shouted as His Majesty exhaled His last breath. 'I have defeated the King and all who follow Him! Now is my time to take over the kingdom. Come, everyone! Let us storm through the gates so I can take my rightful place on the throne!' The enemy and those following him gathered up their weapons and proceeded toward the kingdom's gate, only to find the most horrific sight imaginable.

"'Nooooo! It can't be! How are you here? I saw you die!' Antipalos bellowed as he saw His Highness standing in the entrance. 'You're right,' He replied. 'I did indeed die. But life is more powerful than death. I have overcome death. You have no more weapons to use against me or my subjects. I have, once and for all, paid the price for humanity's crimes so that all who wish to enter the kingdom may do so once again. All that is required is to accept my payment for their crimes.' Antipalos looked down and saw a public path leading to the kingdom's gate that anyone could now take. 'Impossible!' Antipalos said, grinding his teeth in anger. He and his enemies tried to crush the path leading to the kingdom's gate, but they could not. It is indestructible. The enemy and his followers fled the scene infuriated. His Highness was victorious."

"Evil never wins!" Archer shouted with a fist pump.

"Not in the end, at least!" Franklin added. "That's not the end of the story, though. The most wonderful part is this, Archer. *You* are now victorious. By accepting His payment for all the mess ups you've committed and will ever commit, you can now enter the kingdom and live with Him forever. What do you think about that?"

Archer's eyes lit up, and his heart swelled with joy. "I think that sounds amazing!"

"Wonderful!" Franklin exclaimed.

"I will say, it still feels a little cheap," Archer replied. "I didn't do anything, and yet I get to reap all the benefits."

"This is an understandable feeling," Franklin said. "However, what's happened has happened, whether you accept it or not. His Highness decided to provide a path back into the kingdom out of the goodness of his heart. It would actually be *unfair* for you to deny the justice that's already been done. Think about it this way: the victims whose crimes have been repaid and whose wounds have been healed would go back to having the crimes done against them go unpunished and their wounds reopened. I know that's not what you're saying, but that would be the implications of not accepting the justice His Highness has done."

"I obviously don't like the idea of that," Archer replied.

"Any clear-thinking person wouldn't," Franklin replied. "But that's the reality of the situation. So what it ultimately means is that you, me, and everybody else are now forgiven." Franklin clapped his hands together in excitement.

"I am forgiven," Archer said aloud.

"Indeed you are," Franklin replied. "And this leads me to your father. You said earlier that you wanted your father to be punished for hurting you and Nicole. Do you still feel this way?"

Archer thought about the question. "You know," Archer finally replied, "I really don't anymore. I just feel bad for him. I'm not sure what's changed my opinion, though."

"What's changed," Franklin replied, "is your heart after hearing His Highness' free gift of forgiveness. You now realize that we are all bad people after listening to the suffering that His Highness endured because of our mess ups. Everyone is in the same boat, I'm afraid to say. We were all in dire need of a savior and His Highness saved us. Those who accept this are able to experience true love for every human because we realize none of us could enter the kingdom without Him paying our fines for us. Only by the King's payment," Franklin bowed, "is anyone, including you and including your father, able to enter the kingdom."

Archer's heart softened even more toward his father.

"In the end, it's quite simple," Franklin said. "All you have to do is confess that you have made mistakes in your life, admit that you're unable to pay back the fines for those mess ups, and accept the fact that His Highness has already made the payment of your fines."

"That's it?" Archer asked.

"If you do so with an honest heart, that's all it requires to enter the kingdom," Franklin said. Franklin leaned in close to Archer. "Now it's up to you to make that choice. Do you accept His payment for your mess ups and wish to pledge your allegiance to Him, Archer?"

"I do," Archer said, confidently and freely.

"Great!" Franklin exclaimed as he hugged his grandson.

Archer and Franklin stood up and began walking toward the kingdom. "All you have to do is keep following the path that leads to the open gate," Franklin said. "I'll be right behind you the whole time."

Archer took off in the kingdom's direction. *I'm finally doing it*, he thought to himself. His whole life flashed before his eyes. The shame and guilt of his previous mistakes, along with the pridefulness from his achievements, began to loosen their grip on his soul as he approached the kingdom's gate. He started to appreciate every moment that led him to this point.

Archer increased his pace to that of slow jog. *I really* want *to see Him!* he thought to himself. He began to run faster. The town got closer and closer. *I can't wait any longer! I* need *to see you* now!" he shouted. Archer began to sprint as fast he could.

The people and buildings beside him turned to one big blur. Finally Archer reached the end of the path and fell into the King's open arms.

CHAPTER 10

Inside the Walls

"Welcome home, Archer," the King said as Archer wept. "It is so good to have you here. I've been longing for this moment."

Tears continued to stream down Archer's face. "It's so good to be here, Your Highness," Archer replied. "It's like every weight that's ever been on my shoulders is gone. I'm truly and completely happy."

The King smiled upon hearing these words. "Come inside, Archer. I want to show you around your new place of residence."

Upon entering, Archer observed beautiful natural scenes, including a gently flowing stream flanked by many different kinds of flowers bursting with intense colors the likes of which he had never seen. "Oh my goodness!" Archer exclaimed, approaching a group of flowers. "This is the most beautiful blue that I have ever seen in my life. All the colors are so brilliant! Oh, and the aroma! I've never smelled anything so sweet!"

"Isn't it wonderful?" the King replied. "The earthly realm is not what it appears to be. In fact, 99 percent of the physical matter your earthly body sees, touches, and tastes is just empty space. Here, there is no empty space. You are experiencing my creation in its fullest, most complete form."

"Wow," Archer said in amazement. "Everything is just so beautiful."

"Indeed," the King replied. "I wish to share this beauty with all my subjects. Unfortunately many have been convinced that the 1 percent they experience on earth is the most complete form of life. It saddens me that they are only scraping the outermost surface. Come," the King said to Archer, "allow me to show you more of the kingdom."

The two of them walked back to the golden path and went toward the neighborhood. "This," the King said, "is where all my subjects reside. One unified community."

"These houses are amazing!" Archer said. "Look at the jewels around all the doorways. And the gardens in all the backyards!"

"And best of all," the King said, humorously, "no HOA dues to pay."

"Hello, Archer!" said a woman watering her flowers.

"Grandma Ruth!" Archer said as he ran and embraced her in a hug.

"Welcome home, Arch," Franklin said, watching from his rocking chair on the porch.

"Were you even old enough to remember me before I moved here completely?" Ruth asked Archer.

"Barely," Archer replied. "But that doesn't matter! I'm here now with you, and it's so wonderful."

"It truly is," Ruth replied. "You know? I would invite you in for supper, but I wouldn't want to make you late for the party!"

"Party?" Archer asked.

"Of course!" Ruth exclaimed. "There is nothing more worth celebrating than someone returning to His Highness!"

"Ruth is right," the King added. "We should begin to head toward the town center. You don't want to be late to your own birthday party, do you?"

"I suppose not!" Archer said. "Will you two be there?"

"You betcha!" Franklin exclaimed. "We wouldn't miss it for the world."

Archer and the King passed through the neighborhood and approached the town center. "Are you kidding me?" Archer exclaimed as he saw the throngs of people. "All of this is for me?"

"It sure is!" the King replied. "You and everyone else that decided, this day on earth, to come home to me!"

Archer looked down and noticed that the golden path had turned into a red carpet. "Follow it, Archer," the King instructed. "I'll see you up on stage."

Archer strolled down the red carpet, high-fiving those who lined the velvet ropes.

"Archer! Over here!" he heard.

"Grace! Ty!" Archer shouted. He ran over to his friends. "Thanks so much for coming!"

"Come on, man!" Ty said. "You really think we have anything better to do? This is the pinnacle of things worth celebrating!"

"He's right!" Grace said. "Now get up there with the other new members! The ceremony is about to start!"

"You two are the best!" Archer said as he hugged them and rushed up to the stage. Archer promptly found the seat with his nameplate on it and sat down.

"Hey, Archer," said the girl to his right. "This is pretty crazy, isn't it?"

"Oh, hey, Michelle!" Archer said, recognizing her from earlier. "It sure is crazy. It's been the best day of my life by a country mile, though."

"Same here," Michelle said, smiling.

"Welcome everyone!" the King said as He stood at the podium.

The crowd quieted down.

"Today we celebrate the group of people seated behind me who have decided to come home."

The crowd erupted in cheers at these words.

He continued, "As these brave men and women behind me have come to realize, true leading comes through serving. True victory comes through admitting defeat. True perfection comes from admitting one's imperfections and putting on my perfection. The human soul longs for everlasting perfection because that is what I created them for. This is analogous to a dog who longs for the ball to be thrown by its owner. That dog has its eyes locked on the ball and pays no attention to anything going on around it. Once the ball has been released by its owner, the canine sprints with all its might to retrieve the ball.

"However, many humans have been enticed by the wrong ball. They chase after things that could never bring everlasting perfection, wholeness, or completion. These humans don't recognize the longing for eternity that I placed in them as a matter of the spirit. Instead, they are taught to use words like *determined* and *driven* to provide an earthly explanation for their longing to fill inner emptiness. Chasing money, popularity, power, sex, and all the rest, simply are not the cure for what tugs at a person deep inside. Sure, they may bring positive emotions for a little while, but just wait a day, a month, a year. They'll disappear. When you disappoint anything but me, you are shown no forgiveness. It's a meaningless, hopeless way to live.

"Allow me to elaborate," the King continued. "A person who seeks perfection by chasing money will ultimately feel poor because they can never have enough to be satisfied. A person who chases popularity or sex will ultimately be left feeling unwanted and ugly because they will age, lose sexual appeal, and be forgotten. A person who chases being smart will ultimately be left with a crippling feeling of stupidity when the inevitable problem comes along that they can't solve. Yes, chasing after anything but me is like a parasite that feeds on your insides. The more it is fed, the bigger it gets and the more food it demands until a human's last day when it bursts forth from inside of them and abandons them in their most dire moment of need."

Archer was disgusted at the imagery, but this was a much nicer way of putting it than the reality of what happens to a human.

He continued, "Anything that drives a person to leave the kingdom and remain outside is ultimately promising salvation. It takes real strength and courage to turn to away from the false salvation they dangle in front of them. 'Salvation from what?' a person may ask. Salvation from depression. Salvation from feelings of worthlessness. Salvation from ugliness. Salvation from loneliness. Salvation from eventual earthly death and eternal hardship. You see, seeking deliverance from these things is *good*. I don't want anybody living with overwhelming feelings of guilt, shame, and hopelessness. But *I* am the only one who can cure the ailments of the soul. Only *I* can deliver eternal salvation. This is the offer that my sons and daughters behind me have accepted this day."

The crowd stood on their feet and erupted in applause.

"And so I will end my speech by asking that we celebrate everyone seated on stage. They have died to their selves and have reborn as new creations. Today is their kingdom birthday! They have joined my team and donned my golden yoke. They have finally chosen to become like noble horses."

The crowd rose to their feet and roared once more.

Archer looked at his shoulders and could now see that he was, indeed, wearing a brilliant, golden yoke. It felt light and comfortable to him.

"Welcome home, my beloved children," the King said to conclude His speech. The King proceeded to embrace everyone on the stage that day, including Archer.

The kingdom's choir sang a beautiful song as those on stage proceeded down the stairs and into the crowd to meet with their family and friends.

Archer walked to his section where he greeted Grace, Ty, Franklin, Ruth, and other family members.

"Congratulations, Archer," Franklin said as he hugged his grandson. "I am just so happy right now! So many things could have gone wrong and prevented you from ever being here, but here you are. His Highness is truly in control!"

"I'm thankful, too, Grandpa," Archer replied. "I don't think I would be here if it weren't for you."

"Oh no, no, no. I won't take credit for anything," Franklin said. "His Highness deserves all the credit. The only thing I did along the way was just follow orders."

"Yeah, but if it wasn't for you, I would have never heard the message," Archer replied. "I would be who knows where right now! Like, remember when I about drowned in the water that one time? I could have been seriously hurt out there if it wasn't for you!"

Franklin folded his arms and shook his head. "For the second time, it wasn't me. For one, I'm not a great swimmer, and I couldn't have possibly navigated through that storm to find you. Secondly, look behind you."

Archer looked behind him and saw the King. "It was you?" Archer asked.

"It was me," He replied. "I saw that you needed a little assistance and came to help out. That's all."

"Well, thank you, Your Highness," Archer said, smiling. "I really appreciate all that you've done for me."

"You are very welcome, Archer. I love helping my children," He replied. "It's not always me that helps, though. Sometimes I recruit my subjects and work through them. Do you remember the stranger that helped you up the first time you arrived at the Marketplace and were about to be trampled? That was your friend, Ty, here."

"Again?" Archer shouted. "How many times are you gonna save my bacon?"

"As many as it takes," Ty replied. "I'm always ready to be a vessel He can work through whenever He needs me."

"And do you remember the older gentleman that helped you get to class on your first day of college?" the King asked Archer.

Archer's eyes got big and his jaw dropped. "That was you again, Ty?"

"No, not that time," the King replied. "Actually his name is Clive Lewis. He has been a loyal subject for over seventy years and is fine-tuned to hear my requests," the King replied.

"So you told him to stand there and be ready to help me *before* I needed help?"

"Yes," the King replied. "You see, we in the kingdom live outside of the time and space continuum that bounds the earthly universe I created. There is no 'before' and 'after' for us, technically. I am able to communicate with anyone at any time."

"Awesome," Archer replied. "I'll be ready!"

"Very good," the King replied. "I will just mention one more thing, and then your group can return to Franklin and Ruth's house to celebrate your big day. Gold is a wonderful conductor and is resistant to corrosion. My energy and my messages can be more easily transferred to you now that you are wearing a golden yoke. Those with wooden yokes around them have a harder time hearing me and receiving my energy, as wood is a very poor conductor. But more than that, those yokes are a symbol showing what is happening inside of you. Just like fire purifies metal, your acceptance of my payment has purified you, Archer. Your soul has become pure gold without any impurities. You're now a new, perfect, noncorrosive creation. That's all I see when I look at you."

Archer smiled and gave the King a hug. "Thank you, Your Highness," Archer said. "I'll try my best to listen for your voice and serve you however I can."

"That's all I ask," He replied. "Now go have fun with your family and friends! I've got more people to congratulate. Enjoy the day!"

Archer and his group said their final goodbyes to the King and walked back to Franklin and Ruth's house to celebrate.

"Man, what an awesome day," Archer said as Ruth put a piece of cake on his plate.

"Is that big enough?" Ruth asked.

"Oh plenty. Thank you, Grandma." Archer replied.

"So how does it feel, Archer?" Grace asked, taking a bite of her cake.

"It feels so good," Archer replied. "I feel like my whole being is known and loved by all of you and by His Highness. I guess the best way I could describe it is that I feel complete."

"An apt description," Franklin said.

The party continued, and Archer was able to meet many different family members and friends of the family for the first time. He thoroughly enjoyed listening to stories about what life was like in different centuries and in different countries. As time wore on, party goers trickled out of the house until all that was left were Franklin, Ruth, Grace, Ty, and Archer.

"Well," Grace said, "I think we should start to think about heading back too."

"Do we really have to go back?" Archer replied. "It's so nice here!"

"We've still got work to do," Ty said.

"He's right," Franklin said. "Now that you've become a member of the kingdom, it's your duty to spread the message of His Highness to whomever you're called to witness to. For some people, it's close to everyone they meet. For others, it may be that they're just called to live a life that others can see Him through their words and actions. You just have to listen for your orders and obey."

"I understand," Archer said. "After all, it makes me sad, thinking that people are missing out on a relationship with the King."

Everyone bowed.

"I want to share Him with everyone!"

"That's the spirit!" Ruth exclaimed.

"Ready, guys?" Archer asked.

"Ready," Grace and Ty replied in unison.

"Bye, Grandma. Bye, Grandpa," Archer said as the three walked out the front door.

"Bye-bye!" they said.

"Be bold and courageous!" Ruth shouted as they walked down the sidewalk together.

"We will!" they shouted back.

"How do we get back?" Archer asked.

"Just close your eyes and keep walking," Grace instructed. "We'll do it together."

They locked arms and closed their eyes. "Ready?" she asked. "Three...two...one...keep walking."

Archer walked forward with his friends.

"Okay, open your eyes," Grace said.

CHAPTER 11

Extraction

"What I want you to do, Archer, is place your right hand over your heart and read aloud what's on the sheet of paper in front of you. All right, go ahead," Aaron said.

"I, Archer Coleman, believe in His Highness. I believe He sacrificed his life so that I could enter the kingdom. I accept His sacrifice. I solemnly swear to prioritize the kingdom over the earthly, no matter the cost. I shall tell the Truth for the rest of my days."

"Splendid!" Aaron said. "Let me be the first to introduce the newest member of the Truth Tellers: Archer Franklin Coleman!"

The room thundered with applause.

Aaron continued, "I have no doubt that Archer will continue his family's legacy of living a life of service for others and His Majesty." Aaron shook Archer's hand.

"It's an honor to be a member. It feels like it was a long time coming," Archer said.

"We're excited for you to be here," Aaron replied.

"Now we'd like to get you integrated as quickly as possible. So, if you're up to it, we have a brief this afternoon pertaining to a top-level mission that we want you to be a part of."

"Count me in," Archer replied."

"Great. Grace, Ty, we want you two to be there as well. Meet in room 1 in ten minutes."

"Yes sir," Grace, Ty, and Archer said in unison.

"Meeting adjourned!" Aaron announced.

"Congrats, man!" Ty said as they returned to their work stations. "Welcome to the Tellers."

"Thanks, Ty," Archer replied. "When do I get to do all the cool mission stuff, like driving invisible cars and speeding away from bad guys?"

"You gotta go through training before you get to that stage," Ty said.

"So, like, in a month or two?"

Grace and Ty laughed.

"No, Archer," Ty said. "We're talking years."

"Years?" Archer exclaimed.

"Archer, it's dangerous out there," Grace said. "One major mistake, and our cover could be blown. The whole operation could be neutralized."

"I guess that makes sense," Archer said.

"And besides," Grace said, "since the three of us aren't going to college anymore, we'll be able to train full-time. So maybe you'll be qualified to carry out solo missions even sooner."

"Sweet!" Archer said. "But why are you two dropping out of college?"

"Less 'dropped out' and more 'kicked out,'" Grace said.

"Yeah," Ty said. "Typically on a rescue mission, like the one where I came and got you, we're taught to wear masks to hide our identity. I decided to keep mine off so you would recognize me right away. Turns out, that may not have been the smartest move. Our communications network received word that they were able to ID my face as we drove away. Your boy is now on America's Most Wanted list. So, suffice it to say, I won't be showing my face at college anytime soon."

"What about you, Grace?" Archer asked. "There's no reason why you can't go back."

"You're right," she replied, "but I want to stay here. This is what I want to do the rest of my life. Some Tellers are incredibly talented at blending into society and providing us with excellent intel. It's a necessary mission, but I'm not one of those people. I spoke to my parents about staying here permanently, and I spoke to leadership about it. Everyone's on board."

"Does that not get you on some kind of watch list? Someone would have to be insane to leave a school like Helmuth with all its prestige and clout, right?" Archer asked.

"You forgot one important point," Grace replied. "Schools like Helmuth are so arrogant that they feel good when a person like you or me drops out. *Another kid that couldn't take the heat. We are so elite!* they think."

"Gross," Archer said.

"Exactly," Grace said. "So I'm not worried about being targeted just yet," Grace said as she looked down at her watch. "All right, we should start heading toward room 1. The brief is about to start."

"Good call," Ty said. "Wouldn't want Archer to be late on his first day on the job!"

The trio walked over and entered room 1. "As everyone comes in," Sasha announced, "make sure to pick up a packet and a pen. This packet will contain all the details we'll be discussing."

Archer grabbed the materials and sat between his friends in the middle of a long table, big enough to sit around twenty people.

"I believe that is everyone now," Sasha said. "Once we close the doors and the blinds, we may begin."

The room darkened, and a projector screen unraveled from the ceiling. The screen lit up with a presentation titled "Nicole Coleman Rescue Mission."

Archer nearly spit out the water he was drinking.

"Archer," Sasha said, "we believe that you are an integral part of this mission. We understand that this is sensitive with it being your mother, so we have decided to leave it up to you. Do you wish to participate in the rescue mission of Nicole Coleman?"

"One hundred percent yes!" Archer said without hesitation. "I wish to participate no matter how dangerous or however long it takes."

"Very good," Sasha replied. "Let us begin." Sasha clicked the remote controlling the presentation. *Click.* "The first week a person has been admitted into a reeducation camp is the most crucial window to rescue them. Not only are we trying to liberate the person from their captors, we are trying to liberate the person from themselves. What I mean is many rescue attempts have failed due to the person refusing to leave. The indoctrination lessons begin to take hold in their minds, and they often develop an early form of Stockholm syndrome. Therefore we need to move quickly before Nicole has been force-fed too much propaganda so that she can have a reasonable chance of choosing to come with us."

Click. "For those of you who are new, pay attention to the way I worded that last sentence. I said they 'choose to come with us.' The most important aspect of our rescue missions is that we do not, I repeat, DO NOT bring back targets against their will. Our main objective is to mirror the kingdom and follow His Highness. His Highness gave us all free will to enter back into the kingdom. He did not force us to return, and we are not going to force any person to come back with us. Only under rare and extreme circumstances of imminent danger are we to extract the target against their will. Luckily reeducation camps tend to treat their captives well. I have never seen anyone in this nation ever classified as being in imminent danger in the decades that I have worked here. We monitor reeducation camp activity daily by way of infiltrated spies, and they regularly inform us that their methods are strictly educational."

Archer felt relieved that his mother was not at risk for any physical harm.

"So, Archer," Sasha continued, "suppose you are part of the rescue team, and you reach your mother, you and the team make it past security forces. You've done the hard part. You now begin to chat directly with Nicole, and she decides that she will never, under any circumstance, come back with you. She claims you are a liar, a traitor, and an enemy of the state. I want you to hear me right now that you are *not* allowed to extract her from the camp. Do you understand?"

Archer remained silent. He could not bear the thought of looking back and seeing his mother in person for possibly the last time.

"Archer Coleman, do you understand?" Sasha asked again.

Archer closed his eyes and sighed heavily. "I understand," he replied.

"Very good. You're a brave young man. You must come to grips with the fact that she may never come back. I recommend meeting regularly with our resident psychologist to learn cognitive methods for processing this rescue mission in a healthy manner," Sasha said.

Click. "We have received word that Nicole has been admitted into the maximum security reeducation camp in Capital City. I can only assume this is due to who her father is. This makes the mission much more difficult but not impossible. We have extracted targets from this location before, and we can most definitely do it again. With His Highness on our side, nothing is impossible."

Many in the room nodded in agreement.

"And just to emphasize this point," Sasha said, "I'd like to ask Paul to come up to the podium. Paul spent five months at the very same maximum security camp before escaping in the most, shall I say, unconventional way. If you would, Paul, please speak a little bit about the camp, your experience there, and how you escaped."

"Gladly," said the gentleman sitting directly across from Archer. He lumbered along to the podium. "Hello, everyone. As Sasha mentioned, my name is Paul Silvanus. I was rescued nearly two years ago and have worked here ever since. My family did not belong to the Truth Tellers in any way, shape, or form. I grew up in a typical household and had a typical childhood. We were taught the benefits of the HQ system, and I took an interest in the system at a very early age. I eventually went off to college and became a high school teacher, where I taught the ethics of HQ for many years. As the years went by, my beliefs about the HQ system and disdain for all spiritual matters ossified.

"I began volunteering as a community watchdog to sniff out Truth Teller activity and report it to the local authorities. In fact, I hold the record for most Truth Teller members uncovered in a calendar year. It's not something I'm proud to admit, but it's a very real part of my past." Paul's voice shook, and he paused for a few seconds. He cleared his throat and began again. "So one day a few years ago, I was out following a hot lead to try and get picture evidence of suspected Truth Teller activity. I followed one of the suspects to the park and waited for the other to arrive. There I was, parked on the side of the street in the front seat of my car with heavily tinted windows and a digital camera, ready to document any suspicious activity.

"Just as I was about to take a picture of the two suspects converging in the park, the driver's side of my car was sideswiped by an eighteen-wheeler."

Archer gasped.

"Glass went flying in all directions. Airbags inflated. Metal was crunched. I went unconscious immediately and was in a coma for three months. This was the best thing to ever happen in my life." Paul smiled.

"While in the coma, a brilliantly dressed man would approach me over and over, to ask why I was harming him. So I says to him, 'I don't even know who you are!'

"'I am the one the Truth Tellers speak about. When you wake up, go to the same park where your car was struck. There you will find the two men whom you were chasing. Tell them of your experience with me, and they will tell you what you must do.' When I awoke from the coma, I was nursed back to health and did exactly what I was told. I had to, right? How could I not? So I approached the two men cautiously, and they guided me to the local Truth Teller headquarter where I was taught the truth about His Highness. Their description of Him was the exact same as the man I met while in my coma. I was blown away. So I dedicated my life to the King right then and there."

Everyone in the room bowed.

"To make a long story short," Paul continued, "I began work as a Truth Teller educator and was discovered by the authorities. I was sent to the Capital City reeducation camp because I had previously been such a loyal servant to the HQ system. They viewed me as the ultimate traitor. Their tactics, as Sasha said, are strictly educational. Many of my classes revolved around reason, ethics, and science. They do a masterful job of pitting these topics against His Highness and the kingdom. 'Science has conclusively disproven the existence of a spiritual realm,' they alleged, over and over. I now know that the two are inseparable.

"So, after many, many sessions, I came close to my breaking point until, one day, while I was outside during our recreation period, a massive earthquake struck. The violence and the shaking had to have lasted at least a few minutes. I watched as the exterior wall of a building collapsed onto the chain-link fence surrounding the complex. I heard something inside of me say, 'Go and be free.' The earth was still shaking tremendously at this point, and I was scared to move. Miraculously, though, I walked out of the complex as if the ground was completely still under my feet. The guards around me didn't even see me as they were too preoccupied with the earthquake and staying alive. I then walked to the nearest town, about a mile away, and met with a couple that had been told I would be there soon. They housed me and transported me here, where I have been teaching about the kingdom ever since. Praise be to His Highness!"

Applause filled the room.

Paul stepped down and waddled back to his seat.

Archer felt like he was sitting across from a celebrity.

"Thank you, Paul," Sasha said. "What a wonderful testimony shining light on the ultimate rescue mission that His Highness embarked on to save all of us."

"You got that right," Paul said.

Click. Blueprints of the Capital City reeducation camp appeared on the screen. "As you can see," Sasha said, "the living quarters are located deep in the interior of the complex. This has made it extremely difficult for our team to extract captives. Now, if you remember, Paul mentioned that he was able to escape during outdoor recreation time. This has been the most successful method of extraction from Capital City camp as of recently. Thanks to modern camouflage technology, members of our stealth team are able to go right up to the fence and communicate with those inside during their allotted outdoor time. Prisoners are then provided with micro hearing devices, called a Metanoia, that they can insert into their ears. This creates an avenue whereby we can communicate with them and plan out the details of their extraction, if they so choose to accept our help."

Click. "So, with all that said, we are planning to send our stealth team out there tomorrow."

"Tomorrow?" one of the leaders closest to the podium exclaimed.

"Tomorrow," Sasha confidently replied. "Time is of the essence. They are going to put Nicole under a severely heavy learning experience. Every course that she is forced to endure could be the one that pushes her over the edge. This is especially true because we are currently unaware of any belief in His Highness that she may harbor. Archer, can you confirm this?"

"I can confirm that," Archer said. "I've never heard her or Dad talk about the kingdom in a positive light. They always harped that we should listen to our teachers and follow the HQ. The only thing I can think of importance was that she saved a letter that Grandpa had written to me. She said that she felt like it was something that she should do. I don't believe it was because of some secret belief in His Highness, though."

"Thank you, Archer," Sasha said. "Our research has led us to the same conclusion. Thus she is likely to put up little to no resistance to their education. We need to act quickly before she is too far gone for our methods to work successfully. Therefore I have decided to send stealth members to contact Nicole tomorrow. Prisoners currently inside the reeducation camp will help us get Nicole into position where she can communicate with our stealth team. If all goes well, she will have a Metanoia by the end of the day tomorrow and hear her son's voice once again. Do you think you can talk to her, Archer?"

"Of course I can," he replied. "I'm not really sure what I'm supposed to say, though. I don't have any training yet."

"Your personal story is the best tool you can utilize," Paul said. "Just tell her what you've experienced."

Archer nodded his head. "But what about the rescue plans?" Archer asked. "I'd have no idea what to tell her regarding that issue."

"We are working around the clock to plan all that out," Sasha replied. "Don't worry. The plans will be communicated to you once they are finalized, and you can pass them along to your mother at the right time. Right now, establishing a line of communication with her is our main goal. Extraction cannot take place if this crucial step is not executed."

"Is there anything I can do in the meantime?" Archer asked.

"All you can do right now," Sasha replied, "is ask His Highness to help guide our stealth team and provide them with the strength they need to carry out the mission. In fact, let's all take a moment to ask His Highness these things so that Nicole may, one day, come face to face with Him and accept His free gift of citizenship into the kingdom."

Everyone in the room closed their eyes and asked these things.

"Thank you," Sasha said after a minute. "This brief is now adjourned. The packets you received are to stay locked inside of your desks, and you are not to speak about this mission to anyone outside of headquarters."

Everyone arose from their seats and exited the conference room.

As Archer was walking with Grace back to her desk, he heard someone say, "Hey, kid."

Archer turned around. "Hi, Paul. What's up?"

"Kid, I just want you to know that everything's gonna be okay with your mom," Paul said reassuringly. "The authorities talk a big game, and they think they're so smart with their fancy techniques and methods, but a blind person could see right through everything they teach. They don't hold a candle to the Truth."

"Thanks, that means a lot," Archer said.

"Anytime," Paul said. "And, hey, if worse comes to worst, the sufferings of this life are nothing compared with the glory we'll experience living with Him in the kingdom. Ultimately, it's Him that will make the necessary moves happen with your mom when they're supposed to. Whether that's in the earthly or the spiritual realm, that's up to Him."

"You know what?" Archer replied. "You're right. Thanks." Archer felt a sense of peace blanket over his fear.

"I know I'm right," he said with a smile. "Well, I've gotta get back to work. I'll see you two around. Bye now."

"Bye, Paul," Archer and Grace said.

"What a smart guy," Grace said as they continued toward her desk.

"I know, right? He should write a book or something," Archer replied.

"Actually he's written a couple. We use them as teaching material."

"Impressive," Archer said as he sat down on a chair next to Grace's desk. "I'll have to check those out sometime. But right now, I wanna figure what I'm supposed to do for the rest of the day. I've got all this newfound kingdom energy, you know? I wanna fight! Let me at 'em! Let me at 'em!" Archer began to punch the air like a boxer.

"All right, calm down, Ali," Grace replied. "I think it would be best if you took it easy for the rest of the day. Think about all that you've been through! Your family is in disarray, you're on the run from the authorities and, most importantly, you dedicated your life to His Highness! All before dinner! Oh, and not to mention," she said as she batted her eyes, "you got the girl."

"Okay, first off, my boxing style is definitely more Tyson than Ali, so let's set the record straight on that one," Archer said.

Grace rolled her eyes.

"Second, you're right. It's been the most up-and-down, crazy, roller-coaster of a day. I mean, we're talking the highest highs and lowest lows of my life."

"Exactly!" Grace said. "Your hormones have taken a roller-coaster ride too! Imagine what that does to a body. I personally think it would be wise to just recap the day a bit and give your body time to process everything."

"You're probably right," Archer said with a sigh.

"I'm glad you see it my way, snookums," Grace said.

Now it was Archer who rolled his eyes.

Grace laughed. "We'll work on pet names another day. So if you head down that hallway over there," she said, pointing, "we have dorm-style rooms with two sets of bunk beds in each room. I believe they've gotten room 8 all situated for you."

"Sounds good," Archer said. "Thanks for everything."

"It's my pleasure, Archer," Grace said. "I'm just glad you're here, safe and sound."

They hugged.

Archer's eyes shot open during the hug as a thought registered in his brain. He separated himself from Grace enough to where they could look each other in the eyes. "So this means that you and me are—" He struggled to get the words out of his mouth. His mouth moved but didn't make any noise.

"Come on, you can do it," Grace said.

"You and me are...boyfriend and girlfriend?"

"Yup," she said. "That's what you want, right?"

"Only for the last decade! YAHOOOOO!" he shouted.

Grace grabbed the sides of his face and kissed him, partially because she wanted to and partially to keep him from shouting anymore and embarrassing her further. They detached their lips and hugged again.

"You don't know how long I've wanted to do that," Archer said.

"Just as long as I've wanted to," Grace replied.

"Get a room!" Ty shouted from behind them.

Archer's face blushed.

"Oh shut up. You're just jealous!" Grace shouted back.

Ty pretended like he was about to puke. "Not even almost," he said as he approached the two of them. "It's time for you to go to bed, Romeo. We've gotta have you well-rested for tomorrow. Follow me, and I'll show you where our room is."

"*Our* room? You mean we get to be roommates?" Archer said. "Best news ever!"

Grace shot a look at Archer with narrowed eyes.

"I mean...besides...oh geez."

"Come on," Ty said, laughing. "Let's get you to bed while you're still on everyone's good graces."

"Good thinking," Archer replied.

Grace and Archer kissed good night, and Ty led the way to their room.

"Tomorrow's a very important day, Arch," Ty said, opening their bedroom door. "The chances of extracting Nicole increase exponentially, if we're able to get her to listen to you. We need you to be in the right frame of mind if and when that communication line is opened."

Archer followed Ty into the room. He pushed Ty aside. "I call top bunk!" he said, clinging to the ladder.

"ARCHER! Get down here!" Archer froze. He had never heard Ty speak to him in this tone. He slowly climbed down the ladder and looked at Ty.

"I'm sorry for shouting," Ty said. "But I don't think you understand the gravity of the situation. We often only get one shot to communicate with prisoners. The consequences of a failed operation are devastating. Your mom could be lost to the system forever, if this doesn't go right."

"Ty," Archer said, putting his hand on his friend's shoulder, "I appreciate your concerns, man. I'm worried, too, believe me. But it's like Paul said: 'the King's in control.'"

The boys bowed.

"And that brings me a lot of hope that everything will work out like it should."

Ty bobbed his head up and down. "You're right. I could probably afford to loosen up a bit."

"That's the spirit! Que será, será, amigo," Archer replied.

"I'd still like for you to prepare as best as you can, though," Ty said. "And that includes getting a good night's rest. There are clothes in the drawers right over there, and we've got a shower at the end of the hall with new toothbrushes and toothpaste under the sink. Do what you need to do to feel cleaned up and comfortable."

"Thanks, man," Archer said. "Are you going to bed now too?"

"No, I've got a couple more things to get done before I hit the hay, so I'm gonna be up for a bit longer. Is there anything else you might need or any other questions you have?"

Archer thought to himself. "Just one more thing. It's pretty serious, actually. After all the stuff that's happened today, I just can't get this one thought out of my mind."

"Absolutely, Arch," Ty said. "What is it?"

"No," Archer said dramatically. "I've changed my mind. I can't say it."

"Come on!" Ty exclaimed. "We've known each other forever. You can tell me anything."

Archer sighed. "Okay," he said softly. Archer slowly leaned in close to Ty. He looked around the room to make sure no one was within earshot and said, "Can I have top bunk?"

"Good night, Archer," Ty replied as he turned around and walked toward the door.

"I'm taking that as a yes!" Archer said as Ty shut the door behind him. Archer grabbed a fresh outfit and took a shower down the hall. He put on the new set of clothes and brushed his teeth before he returned to his room and climbed into bed. Immediately, a wave of sleepiness overcame Archer as he lay his head on the pillow and pulled the sheets over him. "Thank you for the best day of my life," Archer prayed as he fell into a deep, well-deserved sleep.

"Hello, Archer," Franklin said.

Archer sat up from the bed and rubbed his eyes. He looked around the room.

"This is our guest bedroom," Franklin said. "His Highness has instructed me that you were to come back to the kingdom, and that I was to inform you of your mission."

Archer pulled the covers off his body and sat on the edge of the bed with Franklin. "No, I already know my mission. We had a brief about it and everything. Very official," Archer said regally.

"That's only your earthly mission," Franklin replied. "You've been tasked with meeting your mother in the Marketplace."

"Why me?" Archer asked.

"It's simple," Franklin replied, "you are the person from the kingdom that she will be the most open-minded with."

"There's no way she'd rather listen to me than you," Archer said.

"It's true, Archer. His Highness looked into her heart, and this is what He saw."

"All right then," Archer replied. "If that's what's best for her, then I'll do it."

"Very good," Franklin said. "We should head toward the gate now and get you to the Marketplace."

The two walked down the stairs and turned toward the front door of Franklin's house.

"Don't you dare let him leave without giving his grandmother a hug and a kiss!" Ruth said from the living room.

"I would never!" Franklin exclaimed. "We almost snuck past her…make it quick," he whispered to Archer.

"Good luck, Archer," Ruth said as she embraced her grandson. "Speak the Truth with love, and all will work out how it is supposed to."

"Thanks, Grandma. I'll try my best."

Archer and Franklin stepped outside and began walking toward the kingdom's gate.

"Good luck, Archer!" Franklin's neighbor shouted from his porch.

"We're praying for you!" said another.

"Thank you!" Archer shouted back. Archer looked at his grandfather. "Does everyone here know about everything that goes on?"

"Pretty much," Franklin replied. "You'd be surprised how fast news spreads when you live outside of time."

"Good point," Archer replied.

"Here we are," Franklin said as they approached the gate.

Archer gazed into the bleak, dreary landscape that lay outside the kingdom.

"I've been given strict orders not to go with you past this point. This is supposed to be an exercise in your spiritual maturity. It's up to you to navigate through the temptations outside the kingdom and find your mother. Do you think you can do that?"

"I can and I will," Archer said confidently.

"Excellent," Franklin replied. "Be on guard, Archer. Just because you're wearing the golden yoke doesn't mean that you're immune to the tricks of the enemy. The best way to combat these temptations is to stay tuned in to His Majesty's voice while you are out there. He will always inform you of a way out of temptation, if you are listening."

"Thanks, Grandpa. I'll definitely do that," Archer said.

"All right, I'll be quiet now and let you go," Franklin said. "I'll see you when you come back."

"See you when I see you," Archer replied. Archer exited the kingdom.

Immediately his surroundings turned dull and gray. However, his clothes and body had not changed in brightness or color. "Cool," he said, observing his outstretched arms.

Archer proceeded south on the narrow sidewalk near the kingdom. He encountered a denser population of people the farther along he traversed. Not yet to the Marketplace, Archer saw a man lying in the fetal position on the sidewalk. Archer approached him. "Are you okay?"

"Get away from me!" the man shouted. "I don't want your charity!"

"Woah," Archer said, putting his hands up. "I was just trying to help, mister."

"Oh yeah? You wanna help me? Then leave!"

Shocked, Archer left the man and continued toward the Marketplace. "Don't worry," Archer heard deep inside of him. "People must be in a place to accept help before they can be helped. He was obviously not ready. I commend you for your good intentions."

"I sure hope he comes to that place soon," Archer said aloud.

"Just knowing, for one brief moment, that someone cared about his well-being will help him more than you'll ever know."

"Hey you!"

Archer suddenly heard from a woman to his right. Archer whipped his head around to see what was happening. He pointed at himself to see if she was speaking to him.

"Yeah you! Get outa here! We don't like your kind around these parts!"

"Ma'am, calm down," Archer said coolly. "I'm just trying to get down to the Marketplace and meet someone. I don't even know who you—"

Enraged, the woman shouted, "Calm down? Don't ever tell me to calm down! I can't stand people like you that think

THEY'RE SO HIGH AND MIGHTY AND THEN COME DOWN HERE TO TELL US ALL WHAT TO DO! WELL, IF YOU THINK I'M ABOUT TO LISTEN TO ANY OF THE GARBAGE YOU SPEW OUT OF YOUR BIGOTED MOUTH, THEN YOU HAVE ANOTHER THING COMING!"

Archer wiped the spit off his face that flew from the woman's mouth as she screamed at him. "All right, ma'am," Archer said. "You have a good day." He faced forward and continued to walk.

"GOOD RIDDANCE!"

Surprisingly, the woman's words did not bother Archer. All he saw was a hurting person that needed help. He prayed that she would be healed from whatever was ailing her soul.

"I'm very proud of you for the way you behaved, Archer," the King told him internally. "Love those who wish harm on you. They're still your brothers and sisters."

By now, Archer could start to see the flashing lights and attractions of the Marketplace. "Where am I supposed to go?" Archer asked.

"Go to the FAMILY building. Wait for you mother there."

Archer did as he was told. The Marketplace appeared more densely populated with people than he remembered. Archer struggled to squeeze through the crowd of people to reach his destination.

Many more people hurled insults in his direction.

"WHAT I DO IS NONE OF YOUR BUSINESS!" one man shouted.

"You know what? You're technically right," Archer replied. "I'm just here to love you. Thanks for the reminder, friend."

Frustrated, the man said, "OH YEAH? Well…you…you…YOU NEED TO WIPE THAT STUPID SMIRK OFF YOUR FACE AND LEAVE! YEAH! THAT'S WHAT YOU NEED TO DO!" The man high-fived two people passing by and crossed his arms with a smug look on his face.

Archer pretended to look at an invisible watch on his arm. "Oh my stars, would you look at the time. I'm gonna be late for my meeting! Thanks for the reminder to leave! You're a lifesaver, pal!" Archer shook the man's hand rapidly with both of his hands and continued to walk down the busy sidewalk.

The man looked at his hand and saw that it was glowing. He didn't know what to say. "I'M NOT YOUR FRIEND OR YOUR PAL!" he eventually shouted from a distance.

Before Archer had time to think of a comeback, his focus was dragged away by the bright lights of the HQ building.

"Come one, come all!" said an entertainer in front of the building. "Yes, we at HQ have what it takes to fulfill your life's deepest longings! That's what makes us unique among all the other choices here in the Marketplace!"

"It's all a lie, Archer," the King said to him. "Keep walking and pay no attention to him."

Archer tried to walk away until he heard, "You there!" the entertainer shouted, pointing at Archer. "Yes, you! In the white suit. What's your name, son?"

Archer looked at the entertainer. "My name's Archer."

"Archer, let me ask you a question. Can I do that? Can we have a heart-to-heart in front of all these lovely people?"

"Uhh, sure, I guess."

"Get out of there, Archer! He's up to no good!" the King pleaded to no avail.

The entertainer creeped forward through the crowd until he was face-to-face with Archer.

"Archer," he said, "are you happy with your life?"

"Of course I am," Archer said. "I've never been happier."

The crowd booed and hissed at this response.

"Now, now, good people, let's be nice. He's just a boy," the entertainer said, putting his arm around Archer. "Archer, it says here in my records that you paid our fine establishment a visit not too long ago. In fact, according to our handy-dandy happiness charts, you experienced the highest spikes of your life the *exact* moments your HQ score made the biggest jumps! See for yourself!"

Archer took the paper.

"Don't you remember the adrenaline cascading through your veins when you got all those likes and comments on your social media posts about Helmuth? Don't lie now. Kingdom people aren't supposed to lie."

Archer looked at the spike in his happiness corresponding with that day. "Yeah, I remember how good it felt that day."

"Right!" the entertainer said. "And let's think back to the day you listened to Professor Espinoza's wonderful lecture on HQ. Do you remember what you told yourself that day?"

"He's manipulating you, Archer!"

Archer did not hear the King's voice. Archer thought back to that day.

"I'll give you a little hint," the entertainer said. "The magic word of that day starts with the letter P. Come on, you know it!"

Archer couldn't think of anything.

"Purpose! PURPOSE!" the entertainer shouted. "You felt that your life finally had *purpose* that day. You were finally aiming at a clear target. Look at the happiness spike for that day, Archer! I've got it circled in red to make it easy for you."

Archer looked at the graph.

"Am I right or am I right?" the entertainer asked, grinning.

"You're right," Archer said sheepishly. "It's all true."

"Of course I'm right!" he responded. "Archer, I have just been so gosh darn worried about you since you left. I want your life to be one big happiness spike! Wouldn't that be great for Archer, people?"

The crowd cheered and started chanting, "Archer! Archer! Archer!"

The entertainer took Archer by the hand and led him to the front door of the building. "Archer," he said, holding both of Archer's hands, "please tell me you're going to do the right thing. We love you. We just want you to feel happy." The entertainer opened the door.

Archer saw the mansion, the fame, the wife, and the kids he had seen in his previous encounter in the HQ building. Archer took a step inside.

"That's it," the entertainer said.

Archer paused for a moment.

"Please don't go inside!" the King shouted to Archer. "You still have time to turn around! They don't love you! I do!"

"What are you waiting for?" the entertainer said. "You're so close. You might as well go all in!"

Archer looked at him and looked inside the building. His wife and kids were smiling and waving at him. Archer smiled and waved back. He entered the building.

The entertainer immediately shut the door and put his back up against it. "Victory!" he shouted as the crowd erupted in cheers.

Archer found himself in the foyer of the mansion. "Archer, darling!" his wife said as she came running to him. "You've arrived just in time. Your company's stock has hit all-time highs, and the board wanted to send you a little something to show their appreciation. Check it out!"

Archer looked out the front door and saw a brand-new, custom sports car.

"It just arrived from Italy!" his wife announced.

"Sweet!" Archer replied.

"Daddy!" the kids said as they hugged Archer. "We love you!"

"I love you too," Archer said, hugging them back.

"Oh, darling," his wife said, "it's so great to have you back. We lamented that our family would never be whole again. Oh how we despise that royal scum!"

"Royal scum?" Archer asked.

"Oh don't play dumb, darling. The wretched leader of that cult that dragged you away from us."

"You mean the King?" Archer bowed.

Archer's wife and kids covered their ears and fell to the floor. "Don't speak his horrible name, darling!" she said. "You're lucky you rid yourself of him before it was too late."

"But I don't want to rid myself of Him," Archer said.

"I'm afraid it's too late for that," his wife said. "They will never allow you back in the kingdom once they find out what you've done."

Archer felt an intense feeling of shame.

"Don't listen, Archer. You can never be too far gone to come back. I love you too much," the King told him.

Archer did not hear the King's message. He fell to his knees. "Is it true?" Archer asked, covering his face. "Am I kicked out of the kingdom?"

"Yes, darling! They demand perfection, and you have failed."

Archer began to weep. "But I don't want to live here! I want to live in the kingdom and worship the King!"

"Ahh!" his wife shouted covering her ears. "Stop saying that awful name!"

"Think about your mother, Archer. You need to leave and meet her. She's in real danger."

Archer suddenly remembered why he had come to the Marketplace in the first place. He stood up and immediately walked through the front door.

"Noooo!" wife shouted. "Don't leave us again!"

Archer barged out of the HQ building.

"Where do you think you're going?" the entertainer asked.

Archer did not respond as he ran away.

"You'll be back!" he said. "Everyone always comes back!"

Archer kept running until he found a quiet alley. Shame and guilt filled his heart. He sank to the ground and cried. "I'm so sorry," he said through the tears. "I turned against you. I fell for the temptation. I'm so stupid!"

"Archer, it's okay. I've already forgiven you. You should not be condemning yourself like this."

"But I failed! Someone who's decided to follow you wouldn't fail like that!"

"Every single one of my citizens has failed, Archer. This happens, even after gaining citizenship to the kingdom, but I offer endless forgiveness. What's important is that you learn from your mistakes and grow closer to me through them."

Archer cried for a while longer.

"We can continue this lesson later," the King said to him, "but I need you to get up and go to the Family building. It's time to meet your mother there."

Archer wiped the tears from his cheeks and reluctantly stood up. He entered the stream of people moving along the sidewalk. The attractions of the buildings felt stronger to Archer since he had reentered the HQ building. Representatives from each building could practically smell the shame Archer was feeling.

"Don't worry. I'm with you. Just keep moving," the King told him.

Archer looked down at his feet as he walked so he would not be tempted. The flow of people suddenly stopped, and Archer ran into the person in front of him.

"Watch where you're going, foreigner!"

"I'm sorry! I'm sorry!" Archer said as he backed away from the man. Archer looked up and saw that the huge crowd had stopped in front of the FAMILY building.

Streams of people were entering and exiting, causing a traffic jam along the sidewalk.

"Woah, woah, woah," said a security guard in the front. "You've got to get out of here, son. You're not permitted to be on the property."

"This is a lie," Archer heard deep inside of him. "Don't be afraid of their empty threats."

Archer felt emboldened. "Actually," Archer said, "I was told that I *am* permitted to be here. So what I'm going to do is stay exactly where I'm at and wait for who I came for. Thank you."

"Who told you that?" the security guard snapped back.

"Why, the King, of course," Archer said as he bowed.

Everyone around Archer stopped in their tracks and shouted curses.

"You better watch it! You're on thin ice, pal!" the security guard shouted.

"Good thing I've got light skates on!" Archer said, laughing and playfully elbowing the woman next to him.

"Get out of here. Go back to worshipping your myth," she said.

The security guard grabbed his walkie-talkie. "Calling all units. We're going to need backup at the corner of FAMILY and MONEY. I repeat, backup required at the corner of FAM and MONEY. Wormwood, out."

Archer was not intimidated. "I'm just curious," Archer asked the security guard, "what are you going to do to me if I don't leave?"

"You don't wanna know, punk," he replied, poking his finger into Archer's chest.

Archer did not feel anything when he did so. "Mm-hmm. I see," Archer replied.

Just then, a team of around ten heavily armed soldiers arrived on the scene.

"Remember," the King told Archer, "none of their weapons can harm you, if you don't let them. Be bold."

"Cute uniforms!" Archer told the lead officer. "Where can I get one?"

The lead officer ignored Archer. "What seems to be the issue, Wormwood?" he asked.

"This man right here, officer. He has been told to leave the premises multiple times, and he refuses to do so."

Immediately the team of armed police officers surrounded Archer. The lead officer looked Archer up and down. He shook his head in disgust. "Why can't you people just stay in your own little gated community?"

"Well, you see, officer," Archer said, "I've been sent here on a mission."

"A mission, you say. And what's the objective of said mission, foreigner?" the lead officer asked.

"It's a rescue mission," Archer replied. "I'm here to rescue my mother."

"See!" shouted Wormwood. "I knew he was up to no good! Arrest that man, officer!"

The lead officer approached Archer until their noses were nearly touching. "You think you can just come in here on my watch and blatantly commit a terrorist act and get away with it?"

Archer was taken aback at his sudden outburst.

"Answer me!"

The circle of armed soldiers tightened around Archer, but he remained silent.

"You have five seconds to tell me what you're thinking, swine!"

Archer thought carefully about his response. "What am I thinking, you ask?" Archer asked.

"Yes!"

"What I'm thinking is that you're in dire need of a breath mint, officer."

"THAT'S IT!" the lead officer shouted as he thrust the end of his baton into Archer's chest.

Archer flinched and expected to be in serious pain. However, he realized, after a couple seconds, that he felt nothing.

"THAT'S RIGHT!" the officer shouted as he continued to strike Archer with his baton. "YOU THINK YOU CAN JUST COME INTO MY TOWN AND NOT EXPECT THE LONG ARM OF THE LAW TO FIND YOU? HAVE SOME OF THIS! AND THIS!"

The soldiers encircling Archer cheered on the lead officer as he continued to strike Archer.

In the meantime, Archer stood in place, feeling nothing. He looked around nonchalantly at the surrounding scenes. A crowd of people had begun to form around the soldiers, shouting, "BEAT HIM UP! BEAT HIM UP! BEAT HIM UP!"

Finally, the officer fell to his knees in exhaustion. "All right," he said while his big belly protracted and retracted. "I'm only stop-ping...because I think that you...have learned...your lesson—"

Archer laughed. "Oh, yes, Mr. big, bad officer. Who knows the life of crime I would have led if it weren't for you?"

"Sarcasm!" Wormwood shouted. "I sense sarcasm! Hit him again!" Wormwood raised his hand up and down to incite the crowd.

"HIT HIM AGAIN! HIT HIM AGAIN! HIT HIM AGAIN!"

The lead officer struggled to get on his feet.

Archer helped him up.

"Thanks," the officer said, still trying to catch his breath.

"Anytime," Archer replied with a wink. "Hey, and this time, I really want to see the anger in your facial expression. Really show those teeth! Okay, action!"

"YOU ASKED FOR IT!" the officer shouted as he slowly raised the baton once more to strike Archer.

Archer watched the baton go up and noticed the front door of the FAMILY building violently swing open over the officer's shoulder.

"MOOOOMMMMM!" Archer screamed as he saw Nicole run out of the building. Archer brushed aside the officer like a feather and burst through the circle of soldiers like a set of café doors on a Western saloon.

"ARCHER!" she shouted back.

"Take my hand, Mom! I'll get us out of here!"

The two pushed and shoved their way through the crowd to each other.

"Just a little closer!" Archer yelled. He stretched out his arm as far as it could reach. "I've got you!" he said, holding tightly to her hand. He pulled his mother close to him. "Whatever you do, don't let go of my hand," Archer told his mother.

"I won't!" Nicole said. "Please, just get me out of here!"

"Kidnapping! He's kidnapping someone!" Wormwood shouted from behind them. "Don't just lie there, officer! Do something!"

The lead officer, still huffing and puffing, weakly shouted, "Come...come back, criminal!"

Archer stiff-armed people out of his way as they headed northbound on the sidewalk. Once they had traveled a good distance away from the FAMILY building, Archer and Nicole slowed their pace to a casual walk to avoid suspicion from onlookers. Nicole wanted to stop for a moment to catch her breath.

"Let's go a little farther, Mom. I know a quiet spot up ahead where Grandpa took me once."

"Grandpa? As in my dad?"

"Yes! I'll explain in a minute. Come on!"

Nicole took a deep breath, and they persisted forward.

The crowd and the buildings began to thin out. Finally they arrived at a small park a fair distance away from the buildings. Archer and Nicole approached a bench on the edge of the serene park and sat down.

"Welcome to the Transcendent realm, Mom," Archer said.

Nicole sat silently.

Archer presumed she was still shaken up from the preceding events.

Archer nudged her. "Did you hear me, Mom? I said—"

"I heard you the first time, honey," she shot back.

"Oh...okey dokey," Archer said. "Message received."

The two sat there, awkwardly, as people walked past. Archer tried to think of ways to break the tension. "You know?" he said. "If you think these flowers are beautiful, just wait until you see the ones in the ki—"

"I'm not going in the kingdom, Archer," Nicole interrupted.

"What do you mean?" Archer asked.

"I meant what I said," Nicole replied. "I'm not going there now, and I'm not going ever."

"But...I...but—"

"Archer, honey," Nicole said, "I love you, and I know you're coming at this with a good heart, but you don't know what I've been through. There's no way I could ever go back to the kingdom."

"Go back?" Archer asked.

Nicole covered her face with her hands and began to cry.

Archer immediately scooted closer to his mother to console her.

"It's okay, Mom. Everything's okay," Archer said.

"No, Archer. *It's* not okay!" she replied. "And *I'm* not okay!" Nicole began to weep audibly.

Archer put his arm around her and held her tight. "Well, even if everything's not okay," Archer said, "I'm here with you, and you're free to cry as much or as little as you need."

Tears continued to flow down her face. Nicole began to pound the park bench in anger.

"Hey! Hey!" Archer said, squeezing his grip around her to constrict her arms. "Calm down, Mom! Let's take it down a couple of notches!"

Nicole squirmed and tried to break loose of her son's grip but could not. She tried with all her might to escape. "Let me go!" she shouted.

"I don't think that's a good idea," Archer replied, still hugging her tightly.

"I AM YOUR MOTHER! Do as I say!" she shouted even louder.

"Shh, keep it down, Mom! You could get me in trouble! People are starting to look over here."

Realizing that her son was much stronger than her and that she would never break loose, Nicole eventually surrendered. Her body went limp.

"You can let go of me, Archer," she said defeatedly. "I'm okay now."

"I think I'll stay here for a minute, just to make sure you've calmed down," Archer replied. "What's gotten into you? I've never seen you like this before, Mom."

Nicole sighed. "I've been here before, Archer. Long before you were born. I was just a child. JUST A CHILD!" she screamed and squirmed again.

"Shh, shh. It's okay! It's okay," Archer said, hugging her tightly again.

Nicole calmed down.

"Good," Archer said. "Now, if you want, I'd really like to hear about your trip here as a child."

"I don't think I want to relive it again," Nicole replied with a blank expression on her face. "It was a nightmare, Archer."

"That's totally up to you if you want to talk about it," Archer replied. "I'll be here for whatever you want to tell me." Archer felt an intense sadness build up inside of him. He began to cry, thinking about the hurt his mother must be carrying.

"Oh honey," Nicole said, now consoling her son. "Don't cry for me, really. I'll be okay. It's silly that I'm even acting like this."

Archer released his hug around Nicole, and she wiped the tears off his face. She took a deep breath and sighed once more. "All right," she said. "Even though I can still see you as a newborn baby in my arms, you're a grown man now, and I should be able to have grown-up discussions with you."

Archer agreed.

She began, "I came to the Transcendent realm as a teenage girl, after your grandfather had left us to fend for ourselves. Oh, I was so angry at him for leaving Mom to take care of us kids all by herself! Anyway, I remember I was having a particularly difficult time coping with his absence the night that I showed up here. I found myself where all the buildings were down there. You know, where you found me?" she said as she motioned southward. "I remember it clear as a bell. I was outside of the UNFORGIVENESS building. It sounds so silly to say it now, but the person out front ran through this whole presentation on how my father was the reason for all my troubles in life. All the sleepless nights. All the anxiety. The whole nine yards. It all made sense to me. So I went inside. Inside, I talked to an agent who convinced me that my best possible life would require never forgiving my father for what he had done to us. I signed their contract, and I immediately felt better. At that moment, I believed I wasn't the reason why he left. I wasn't the one causing my misery. It was all him."

"I see how that could make you feel better," Archer said.

Nicole nodded her head up and down in agreeance.

"So I left the building and went outside to go live my life. That is, until I met *him*," Nicole said somberly. "So there I was, walking along the sidewalk, when I bumped into a man wearing an outfit similar to yours. We began to chat, and he told me about the kingdom, about His Highness, about the love and forgiveness He offers, etc., etc. And boy, did his words seem to renew and refresh my hurting heart. I was interested, for sure. What really hooked me, though, was that he began to tell me more about myself than even *I* knew about myself. I was amazed at the deep, dark places inside of me that he knew about. It was like he was some kind of magician that put me under hypnosis."

"I don't like the sounds of this guy," Archer said.

"Just wait," Nicole replied. "He asked me if I wanted to follow him to this kingdom and, of course, I said, 'Yes!' 'Wonderful!' he said. 'Follow me.' So I did. We headed northbound on the sidewalk. I could almost start to see the kingdom when he took a right turn down a dark alley. I stopped in my tracks. 'Where are you going?' I asked. 'The kingdom's up there! I can see it.' 'Yes, but that way does not lead to the *true* kingdom,' he told me. 'Only *I* have been told the way to the true kingdom. Come!'"

Archer interrupted. "Please tell me you didn't go."

Nicole hung her head low. "I wish I could tell you that, but I followed him."

"No!" Archer shouted.

Nicole continued, "He led me down the alley until we had reached a dead end that contained nothing but a lone dumpster. 'I thought you said this way took us to the kingdom?' I asked. 'Ye of little faith!' he shouted as he shoved me into the wall. 'Don't you believe me? Would I lie to you?' he asked with bright yellow eyes. 'Help me move this dumpster, and I'll show you, you unbelieving woman.' He let go of me, and we both pushed the dumpster over to reveal a hidden trapdoor in the ground. 'Pretty cool, huh?' he said. 'I'm the only person to ever be told where this is.' 'Wow!' I said, 'And this leads to the kingdom?' 'Indeed,' he said as he opened up the hatch. I peered inside, and lots of people were in there. They were all dancing and smiling. They looked so happy. I'll never forget the smiles on their faces.

"'Can't you see now, woman?' he said. 'I've saved your ungrateful and unbelieving life. I only speak the truth that has been sent to me and me alone. I believe you owe me an apology.' 'I'm sorry… uhh…sir. You know what, I just realized, I don't even know your name. What should I call you?' I asked. 'Call me the Prophet,' he replied. 'Okay,' I said. 'Thank you, Prophet.' 'You are welcome,' he said. 'Now you must go inside and meet your new family. Go on, child.'

"So I climbed down the ladder, and the Prophet shut the hatch behind me. Upon reaching the end of the ladder, I was hit with a feeling of euphoria. Everyone was so welcoming and accepting. They exemplified everything that I had ever wanted from my family and friends. They called themselves 'the Community,' and I was immediately integrated into their way of life. It was impressive, Archer. The Community was totally self-sustaining. We grew our own food and made our own clothes. The kids were taught from textbooks that had no outside influence from the 'evil one.' We were completely defended from the evils that lie outside of the Community. There was absolutely no reason to leave our perfect paradise."

"You obviously left, though," Archer said. "What happened?"

"Well," Nicole said, "at one of the Prophet's daily gatherings, he announced plans to grow the Community and attract more members. He was going to handpick a team of us that would be allowed to leave the Community and recruit in the outside world. By that time, I had been there quite a while and had earned the Prophet's trust. I never questioned him and always did what he said because I felt in the deepest part of me that he loved me and would *never* do anything to hurt me. Despite all that, I wasn't chosen as a recruiter. I was devastated.

"'His Highness has personally spoken to me, and He told me that your souls were not pure enough to enter the outside world run by the evil one,' he told all of us that were not chosen. 'You all should be thanking me for not sending you sheep into the wolf's den. I am doing you all a favor, even if it does not appear that way. So continue to follow my instructions perfectly and purify yourselves so that, one day, you might be as holy as the others.'

"And that's exactly what I did," Nicole said. "I tried so hard to purify my soul for the Prophet. I sat in the front row of every daily gathering. I volunteered to work extra shifts in the harvesting fields. I memorized the writings of the Prophet, frontward and backward! But no matter how hard I tried, I was never chosen to be in the Prophet's recruiter group. One day, I worked up the courage to ask why I had not been chosen to recruit new members. 'All I want to do is spread your message of truth!' I told him. 'This is a good desire, child,' he said. "However, His Highness continues to show me the disobedience in your heart. Although you may not show it outwardly, I see the little evil that remains. Purify it, and I will send you out into the world!' So I worked even harder, to the point of total exhaustion. I actually ended up in our little hospital for a few days from overworking my body."

"Now I *really* don't like the sounds of this guy," Archer said.

Nicole continued, "While I was in the recovery ward of the hospital, soldiers showed up at the Community and condemned the whole place. I remember the government officials bursting through the hospital doors and telling us to pack up our things. I can't describe the level of fear I was feeling at that moment, Archer. The Prophet had told us the day may come when the evil one infiltrated and destroyed the Community, leaving us all helpless against his evil schemes. I never believed it would actually happen, but it did, and I was mortified at what they would do to me."

"How did they find the Community, if it was so well hidden?"

"Apparently," Nicole replied, "a government official caught wind of the Community by going undercover and listening to one of the recruiters' speeches. The authorities moved to shut us down once they heard that the Prophet was preaching spiritual matters and that he strictly forbade any of us following the tenants of HQ. That's why the Community was raided and, coincidentally, that's also when I met your father. He was part of the team tasked with clearing the hospital. If I wouldn't have been so scared, I would have been more attuned to his charm and good looks as he grabbed me by the arm and pushed me back up the ladder."

"Love at first shove," Archer said.

"Back on earth, myself and all the Community members were sent to reeducation camps across the country," Nicole said. "I just so happened to be at the location where your father was temporarily stationed. I knew that he was interested in me because he would always stand by me as he transported us from classroom to classroom. Eventually we started to talk to each other, and we developed a friendship over my time there. We would take long walks in the courtyard and talk about anything and everything. He was the one who really helped me understand the manipulative nature of the Prophet. I discovered that the jerk just used me for his own self-importance, in the name of the kingdom.

"I broke down mentally as I processed through all my experiences there. I don't think I would have ever been able to live a sane life, if it weren't for your father walking beside me as I recovered. I owe him so much." A little smile flashed across Nicole's face, thinking about young Henry. "In fact," she said, "I immediately agreed when he asked me to always obey the HQ and swear off any future connection with the kingdom. I felt like it was the least I could do for him."

"Wow. I'm so sorry you went through all of that," Archer said. "But I hope you know that Prophet guy wasn't a part of the true kingdom. He was preaching a false kingdom that doesn't exist, just so he could trick people into following him."

"I see that now," Nicole said, starting to cry. "Oh, Archer, I've been a terrible mother! Your father and I tried so hard to keep you kids from hearing about the kingdom, but I don't even know what's right and what's wrong anymore!"

"Hey, don't say that," Archer replied. "You've been a great mom to us. You did the best you could with the information you had."

"But I didn't do the best I could!" Nicole said. "I ignored the obvious signs that something was wrong with the HQ because I was too worried about you kids not getting hurt by the kingdom like I did!" She put her hands in her face.

"You just did it because you loved us and wanted to protect us. That's what good parents do," Archer said reassuringly.

"Maybe," Nicole replied. "I feel like I should have at least mentioned the possibility of the spiritual to you kids, though."

"What makes you think that?" Archer asked.

"Your father," she replied. "I used to brush off his outbursts against HQ dissenters as righteous anger. But something inside me changed, once he started directing his outbursts toward you. What righteous ideology would cause a father to act that way toward his own flesh and blood? I just couldn't get over that."

"That's a good question," Archer replied.

"So, a few months ago, I did the unthinkable," Nicole said. "I read your letter from Franklin that I had saved. Everything changed for me in that moment, Archer. I could sense the love that he put into the letter. It was just beautiful. I finally recognized the love that he had always shown his family despite all the persecution he was put through. He was always so kind to your father, even though your father treated him like dirt. And you know what? I finally noticed the dichotomy: Franklin's so-called 'threatening' beliefs taught him to accept and love, while your father's 'accepted' beliefs caused him to judge and hate. Juxtaposing their beliefs showed me who the real threat was. So, once again, I had to work up the courage to bring this up with your father, and he became infuriated. I saw something sinister in his eyes, and I got scared. I guess I should have just kept my mouth shut because he never trusted me from that day forward. That was why he tied me up in our bedroom on the day that he planned to have you taken into custody. He was afraid I would say something to blow his cover. Little did he know, though, that I decided to always keep a pocket knife on me at all times, after that tirade."

"Smart," Archer said.

"I tried so hard to cut myself loose once he left me alone, but he tied it so tightly! I'm so sorry I didn't come sooner."

"Mom, you have no reason to apologize. You saved me. Without you, I would have been toast. I'm the one that should be sorry! I left you to deal with Dad all by yourself."

"Oh, he's all hat, no cattle, honey," Nicole said. "I can handle him and any reeducation camp he may decide to throw me into. I'm not scared of him anymore."

"I'm glad to hear that," Archer replied. "Okay, so you're in the reeducation camp down on earth, right?" Archer asked to clarify.

"Correct," Nicole replied.

"Got it," Archer said. "Do you think the stress of being there drove you to come here?"

Nicole pondered the question. "No, I don't think so," she replied. "I'm not scared of the authorities either. They can yell and scream all they want, but it doesn't bother me anymore." Nicole looked straight ahead, expressionless. "You know what does keep me up at night, though?"

"What's that?" Archer asked.

"The picture that I had in my head of our perfect little family unit, growing older together and being best friends and doing everything together is gone. And you know what? I poured my heart and soul into that picture. But someone stole it out of my hands, took a lighter to it, and now it's just a pile of ashes. I feel like my world has fallen apart, Archer. I don't sleep. I don't eat. I don't pay attention in my reeducation classes. I don't really do or feel anything anymore. I'm not *able* to do or feel anything right now. It's the weirdest thing. The only thing I know is that I just want my family back."

"I'm so sorry," Archer said as he hugged his mother. "I love you, and I hope you never forget that I'll always be a part of your little family, Mom. Even if we don't get to see each other very often down on earth, I'm not going anywhere."

"I love you, too, honey," Nicole replied. Nicole sat back and remained in a pensive state for a short time until she finally broke the silence. "Do you think that's the reason I'm here, Archer?" she asked.

"What reason?" he replied.

"Am I too fixated on my family? I mean, I was in the FAMILY building, for Pete's sake. How much more obvious can it get?"

Archer didn't know how to respond. In that moment, the King spoke to Archer, "Tell her that she is indeed correct. Fixating on anything but Me is bound to end in disappointment."

Archer cleared his throat. "Actually, Mom, you're right. Fixating on anything but the King is bound to end in disappointment." Archer bowed. "The King is the only perfect foundation that you can build your life upon that will withstand the floods and earthquakes that are bound to happen." Archer bowed again. He continued, "Think about it: every human is flawed, so if you put your ultimate hope in humans, you're just setting yourself up for failure."

"Wow, that was deep, Archer," Nicole said. "Where did that come from?"

"Not me," he said with a grin.

Nicole did not understand what he meant.

"What I mean is I'm in constant connection with His Highness, now that I've come home to His kingdom. I proudly wear His royal yoke, just like Grandpa. See for yourself. Look at me."

Nicole looked at her son and watched as a shining, golden yoke appeared around his shoulders.

"It's brilliant, Archer," Nicole said. "You know? Now that you mention it, I remember that the Prophet had an old-looking, wooden one around his shoulders that he always tried to break free from, but he never could. It would lock on to him tighter and tighter the more he tried. Oh man, do I remember how badly he hated that thing!"

"I bet he did hate it," Archer replied. "His yoke was probably extremely heavy and burdensome."

"So what does that all mean?" Nicole asked.

"It means that everybody lives for someone or something," Archer replied. "There's no getting around it as a human. It's up to us to decide who or what we live for. And the truth is, there's only one who offers a light and comfortable yoke. And that is—"

"The King," Nicole interrupted.

Archer bowed. "Yes," he replied, surprised by his mother's interjection. "His Highness…did you already know that?"

Nicole shook her head. "No," she replied, "I'm just following the breadcrumbs, and it looks like they lead right to the kingdom's gate."

"The gate is open, and He's waiting for you right now, Mom." Archer asked his mother, "Do you want to see Him?"

Nicole closed her eyes tightly and toiled over her response. "I want it to be true, Archer. I really do," she said. "It makes me feel all warm and fuzzy inside. But that's exactly how I felt living in the Prophet's Community. I trusted a religious man with my life, and I ended up getting hurt. Badly. I promised myself I would never get tricked like that again. And, plus, I made a promise to your father that I would never again entertain the idea of the kingdom."

Come on! Archer said in his head. *You're so close*! Archer prayed to the King. "Please give me the right words to say so that my mom will choose to go see you."

The King responded, "Archer, while I understand you love your mother and want to see her experience the joys of the kingdom, it is not the responsibility of your words to convince her to do anything. Only I am able to change hearts. I simply want you to love her, and I will take care of the rest."

"Okay, I can do that," Archer said aloud.

"You can do what?" Nicole asked.

"Oh, uhh, nothing," Archer said.

"Okay?" Nicole replied. "Anyway, like I was saying, I'm going to have to decline your offer, Archer. I just can't go there right now. Now or maybe ever."

"I'm sorry to hear that," Archer said, heartbroken. "But I understand. I'll still love you, no matter what."

The two sat on the bench quietly for a while and watched the activities of those of the park.

"So," Nicole said, "how do I get back?"

"You're asking the wrong guy for that," Archer replied with a chuckle. "I'm still trying to figure out basic stuff, like how time works up here."

"Well if you don't know, then I should probably ask someone that does," Nicole said. "I really should get back soon."

Archer recalled the times when he returned to the Earthly realm. "I'm trying to think, but I just don't think I know of a surefire way to get back. Usually someone tells me when it's time, and I just kinda find my way back. It's really strange because you'd think I'd have it figured out by now with as many times as I'd been up here. Come to think of it, I—" Archer stopped because he heard snoring. He looked over at his mother. Nicole's eyes were shut, and her head laid on the back of the bench. Her body transitioned from opaque to translucent until it had disappeared from Archer's sight. Archer had never seen this occur before. "I guess when it's your time to go, it's time to go," Archer said. "Talk to you soon, Mom."

Archer returned to the kingdom and was greeted by his grandfather at the gate.

"So how'd it go?" Franklin asked as they walked to his house.

"It went okay," Archer replied. "We talked about some stuff from her past, and I was able to talk about His Highness to her."

"Excellent!" Franklin said. "Did she respond well to it?"

"I would say it was decently received," Archer replied. "But it's a negative on her coming to the kingdom right now."

"That's too bad," Franklin said. "The most important thing is that His Highness planted the seed in her heart through you. We can only pray that the seed will take root, and she will decide to accept her one-way ticket out of prison."

Archer suddenly remembered the stealth team's mission to give Nicole the Metanoia. "Oh no!" Archer said as he slapped his forehead with the palm of his hand. "I didn't tell her about the mission! Now she won't know it's coming, and she'll probably be all freaked out when it happens!"

"Archer, Archer," Franklin said calmly. "Don't worry. Your job was simply to tell her about His Majesty and the kingdom. Now it's up to her to decide what she wants to do. You did everything that was asked of you."

"I sure hope so," Archer replied.

"Trust me, you did. I'm very proud of you."

"Thanks, Grandpa."

"Well, here we are. Home sweet home!" Franklin said.

Archer and Franklin ascended the stairs and entered the guest bedroom. "It's time for you to go back to the Earthly realm as well, Archer," Franklin said. "Just lie down, relax, and close your eyes, and you'll be back in no time at all."

Archer hopped on the bed and closed his eyes. He began to feel very sleepy.

"Be bold and courageous during the mission, okay?" Franklin said. "His Highness is protecting Nicole, so no one who's against her can even come close to her unless it's part of His plan. Remember that! It will give you hope and peace."

"I will, Grandpa," Archer said. "I love yo—" Archer transitioned away, and the guest bed became empty.

"I love you, too, Archer."

CHAPTER 12

The Mission

Archer woke up on the top bunk and sat up. *Bonk*! "Son of a—"

"Good morning, sleepyhead!" Ty said. "Watch your head next time. We've got low ceilings down here."

"I see that," Archer said, rubbing his forehead.

"Come on down, and I'll get you caught up to speed on what's happened today," Ty said.

"What time is it?" Archer asked, descending the ladder.

"It's a quarter to noon, but there's been a lot of action already."

"I slept for that long? I must have been more tired than I thought," Archer said, putting on a new shirt. "Any good news?"

"Yeah, I'd say things are progressing smoothly so far," Ty answered.

"Anything specific to report?" Archer asked as he walked down the hall to brush his teeth.

"Nothing out of the ordinary, thankfully," Ty said, following closely behind. "We've been able to hold constant communication with our lead operator on the inside, and the rescue team is in transit to their post outside the compound. So far so good."

"That's what I like to hear," Archer mumbled with a mouth full of toothpaste foam. Archer finished brushing his teeth, wiped his mouth, and headed toward Grace's desk. "Today's gonna be a good day," Archer said confidently.

"Good morning, Grace!" Archer said.

"Good morning," Grace replied before she kissed him. "Mmm, minty fresh!"

"Only the best for you!" Archer said. "So what's the 411?"

"Right now, the plan is for Nicole to be out in the courtyard around 1800," Grace replied. "She's almost through her morning classes, and then they'll give her a small break for lunch. We're anticipating that to be around 1215. We'll check in with Agent R to see how things are progressing at that point."

"Agent R?" Archer asked.

"Agent R is a Teller," Grace replied. "She voluntarily lives inside the camp and provides us with invaluable intel."

"Who would volunteer to live in a dreadful place like that?" Archer asked.

"Someone dedicated to kingdom work," Ty said. "We're very lucky to have her as an asset."

"That we are," Grace said. "And lucky for us, Nicole was assigned to be her roommate, so we've been able to keep extremely close tabs on your mom."

"That makes me feel better," Archer replied. "Do we know how Mom is doing?"

"Well," Grace replied, "I spoke to Agent R while you were asleep last night, and she was pretty apprehensive about the mission. Apparently your mom had a bit of a mental breakdown yesterday. She cried incessantly after classes. Agent R tried to console her, but nothing was helping. She ended up just sitting there with Nicole until your mom finally cried herself to sleep. I reported this to leadership, and they discussed scrapping the mission and trying another day. They ultimately decided we should go forward with it as planned."

"Good," Archer replied. "As a matter of fact, I interacted with her last night in the other realm."

"You did?" Ty exclaimed. "We need to report this right away! This could change the whole tone of the mission! Come on, let's go talk to Timothy, the mission leader."

Ty led Archer and Grace to one of the offices near the entrance and knocked on the door.

"Come in!" shouted a voice from inside.

Ty opened the door and ushered Archer inside.

"Oh hello, Archer!" Timothy said from behind his desk. "Come in, come in!"

Archer shook Timothy's hand. "It's a real pleasure to meet you, Timothy," he said.

"The pleasure's all mine," Timothy replied. "And I see you've brought along Agent T and Agent G, two of our finest young Tellers. Come in, you two!"

"What's that about us being young, Timmy?" Ty joked as they all sat down. "You're not much older than us!"

"I've still got a few years on you whippersnappers!" Timothy replied. "But you're right. Age doesn't really matter in this case. We're all supposed to set a good example, young or old! Ol' Paul taught me that one."

"Fair point," Ty said.

"Anyway," Timothy said to Archer, "I apologize we didn't get to officially meet yesterday. I got back to headquarters last night after you had already fallen asleep. We just got back from a European meeting with other leaders on the continent."

"Cool," Archer said. "How are things in Europe?"

"You know," Timothy said, "I was in Greece, and the King is doing a great work there."

Everyone bowed.

"There's a lot of suffering, but His light is shining through all of the darkness, if you look for it."

"I love it," Archer said.

"So what brings you all in here?" Timothy asked.

"Ty recommended I talk to you about my encounter with Mom last night, to see if that changes any plans," Archer said.

"Tell me about it," Timothy said as he folded his arms.

"Well, the long and the short of it is that she's pretty heartbroken about how everything has gone down. And who wouldn't be? So we were talking about things, and she shared some stories about her past."

"I'm sure she mentioned her encounters with the Prophet, right?" Timothy asked.

"She did," Archer replied.

"There's nothing that I can think of that angers His Highness more than someone taking advantage of people while using His name as justification," Timothy said. "The repercussions of such actions ripple outward, for a very long time, and for good reason. What person would willingly inquire about the kingdom after an experience like that?"

"Totally," Archer said. "Mom seemed decently receptive when I tried to bring up the kingdom and His Highness, but she said no when I asked her if she wanted to go there with me."

"Understandable," Timothy said. "Did it seem like she felt better after sharing her past with you?"

"I would say so," Archer answered. "She mellowed out the more we talked. And here's some good news! Near the end of our chat, she even said she wanted the story about His Highness and the kingdom to be true. Her past hurts and her promise to Dad were holding her back from believing it, though."

"That is good news!" Timothy said. "I have no doubt that those concerns will melt away in the presence of the Truth."

"Let's hope so," Archer said.

"Does this new information change anything about the mission?" Ty asked.

"Of course it does," Timothy said with a smile. "Now I'm even more confident we'll accomplish our goals."

"But no strategic changes?" Ty asked.

"Not one. We're full-go barring any other dramatic circumstances."

"Ten-four," Ty replied.

"Any other questions or comments?" Timothy asked. "No? All right. I will see you all at 1730 in the Situation Room to follow the proceedings. Try and stay busy until then to calm your nerves, Archer. See you soon."

"Thanks, Timothy," Archer said, rising from his chair. "See you soon."

"What are we gonna do until then, friends?" Archer asked as they approached Grace's work station. "Is there a ping-pong table around here somewhere?"

"*We* are full-time employees here. Grace and I have work to do, friend," Ty said.

"He's right," Grace added. "You see this mountain of paper-work? It ain't gonna file itself."

"What am I supposed to do then?" Archer asked.

"Anything you want," Grace answered. "We've got a little gym and a treadmill over in room 20, if you feel like that would help you. Or you could peruse our library and find a good book to dive into! That could be fun!"

"Read for fun?" Archer asked rhetorically. "Ha! I'd rather wait in line all day at the DMV!"

"Hey, man, readers are leaders," Ty said. "Everyone in the Truth Tellers is encouraged to be a lifelong learner. We've got all kinds of book clubs down here that you should really think about getting plugged into."

"Maybe," Archer replied. "What kind of books are down here?"

"All kinds!" Grace gleefully replied. "Fiction, nonfiction, you name it. The coolest part about our library is that…you know what? Let me just show you. Come on."

Grace led Archer to the end of one hallway. She knocked on the wall in a distinct sequence. Up, down, left, right, center, up, down, left, right, center. Grace stepped back as a small compartment jutted out from the wall. She opened the lid. "Do you remember what to do?" Grace asked.

"I sure do." Archer placed the miniature golden yoke in the slot and rotated 180 degrees.

"What is your purpose?"

"Be a Noble Horse," Archer answered.

"Very well," the voice said. The lid lowered, and the compart-ment slid back into the wall. *Click. Bzzzzz.*

Archer stepped back as the whole wall slid over to his right, exposing a set of stairs leading downward to an open room filled with bookcases.

"Make sure to close the wall behind you and grab your yoke from the box. Just hit the red button on the right once you're completely inside," Grace said as she led the way down the stairs.

"Roger that," Archer replied, pressing the red button. *Bzzzzzz.* The wall slid over to its original resting place. The small compartment jutted out from the wall in his direction, and Archer grabbed his yoke from inside.

"Wow!" Archer exclaimed as he descended into a small room with three full bookcases. "All that secrecy for this cramped place? What if we get stuck down here?"

"Don't worry about that," Grace said, "There are multiple exits down here in case everything on that level got ransacked. We could find our way out."

"Good to know," Archer replied.

"Why so much protection for just a few books?" Archer asked.

"Because," Grace explained, "these are our most prized possessions. Not solely because these books are old and precious to us, which they are, but because of the ideas and Truths contained in them. Ideas and Truths are two of the most powerful resources on the planet, and we intend to protect them at all costs. Most of the texts down here were placed on the banned list during the early stages of the HQ takeover. Authorities nationwide rounded up any book on the banned list and burned it publicly. Also anyone caught with one in their possession was punished and reeducated. Many brave people risked their lives to ensure that these books weren't relegated to the ash heaps of history."

"We sure didn't learn about that in school," Archer said.

"Here, come look at this section," Grace said as she led Archer to the end of the middle bookcase.

"Is that Paul sitting back there?" Archer asked, looking around the end of the bookcase.

"Sure is," Grace said. "He likes to come down here and write. He says it's the only place where he can find some peace and quiet to think."

"It is pretty nice down here," Archer replied.

"Well, speaking of Paul," Grace said, "this section is dedicated to books and letters he's written since his admission into the Truth Tellers. Take a look."

Archer observed the multiple writings of Paul. "*To the Americans*," Archer said as he picked up a book.

"Oh that's one of my favorites," Grace said.

Archer leafed through the pages. He quoted aloud, "'So, my brothers and sisters, you died to the HQ through the body of His Highness, that you may belong to another, to Him who was raised from the dead, in order that we might bear fruit for Him.' What exactly does that mean?" Archer asked.

"Why don't you ask him yourself?" Grace asked. "In the meantime, I've gotta get back to work before the mission starts. Have fun down here!" Grace kissed Archer on the cheek and ascended the stairs.

Holding the book, Archer approached Paul, sitting at his writing desk.

"Hi there," Archer said cautiously, trying not to scare him.

"Oh hey, kid," Paul said. "How are you doing today? Pull up a chair and join me!"

"I'm doing okay," Archer replied, sitting down. "What are you up to, Paul?"

Paul took off his glasses and placed them on the top of his head. "I'm just putting the final touches on a letter I'm sending to some old friends of mine in Greece."

"Cool!" Archer said. "Funny you say that. I met someone this morning, and he said he just got back from Greece."

"Oh good!" Paul exclaimed. "You were able to meet my apprentice, Timothy. He's a wonderful kid and an even better friend. You two will get along really well."

"I concur," Archer replied.

"Which book do you have there?" Paul asked. "Ahh, yes, one of mine. Do you like what I wrote?"

"I just picked it up and read a couple sentences," Archer said. "It seems pretty complicated from the little I read, though."

"Matters of the spiritual realm can become convoluted and confusing very quickly. That's for sure. However, I tried my best to simplify the messages. Take chapter thirteen for example. Can I see it for a second?"

"Sure," Archer said, handing over the book.

Paul flipped to the right page and quoted, "'Therefore, it is necessary to submit to the authorities, not only because of possible punishment but also as a matter of conscience.' You would not believe how much heat I took for writing this. But that's okay because I only write what His Highness desires that I write."

"When does He tell you what to write?" Archer asked.

"His Spirit lives in me," Paul answered, "and I make sure to let that Spirit guide my words and ideas."

"Amazing," Archer said.

"You know what's even more amazing?" Paul asked. "That same Spirit lives inside of you, too, kid. Listen to it. Live by it. Life and peace will fill your mind, if you allow it to be governed by that Spirit. The Spirit is the eternal missing ingredient of systems produced by humans. They live by the flesh alone, and the mind governed solely by the flesh is death. Every time. Trust me, kid, I've been there."

"Me, too, Paul. Me too," Archer said.

"That's one distinction that I always try to make clear in my writings," Paul said. "There isn't technically such a thing as a 'good' person. The term *good* relies on a subjective scale that humans create to judge one another. I prefer the term *righteous*. This takes the subjectivity out of the equation because righteous means perfect and blameless. Either you're perfect or you're not. So when a person accepts the King's ransom for our imperfection"—Archer and Paul bowed—"that person invites His Spirit into their mind, and they actually transition from *dead* to *alive*, not bad to good, as most people think. Do you think any man-made system can do that for us?"

"Definitely not," Archer replied with a chuckle.

"Of course it can't," Paul added.

"Consequently no one can brag about their transition to life because He did all the work! That would be like someone doing all your homework, and you turning it in to the teacher for the credit.

Any sensible person would have difficulty bragging about that A+, wouldn't they? Well that's exactly what He did for us, and I prefer it that way. I'm now able to love myself, those governed by the flesh, and those governed the Spirit equally. It's a beautiful way to live, Archer."

"It sure sounds like it," Archer replied. "What a world we would live in, if everyone thought like that."

"Amen," Paul said.

"Well, kid, I'd love to chat with you some more, but I've got to finish this letter by the time Timothy leaves for his next trip in a couple of days. It was great talking to you. Sign up for my class that I teach throughout the week, and we can continue this discussion!"

"I will definitely do that!" Archer exclaimed.

"Oh," Paul said as Archer was getting up to leave, "best of luck with your mother this afternoon. The Spirit intercedes for the King's people in accordance with the will of the King."

They both bowed.

"Let that give you peace of mind today, no matter the outcome."

"Thanks, Paul," Archer said. "I'll try and remember that. See you around." Archer put the copy of *To the Americans* back on the shelf, ascended the stairs, and exited the library.

"How did it go?" Grace said as Archer approached her desk.

"I feel like I gained a good five IQ points listening to him speak," Archer replied. "That guy is in a league of his own."

"We're lucky he's writing down all of his thoughts," Grace said. "His words will be reviewed for generations to come."

Guuurgle. "Holy smokes," Grace said. "Was that your stomach? Or is there a lonely orca inside of you looking for a mate?"

"Very funny," Archer said. "I haven't eaten anything yet today. It's been so go, go, go from the moment I woke up."

"If you want," Grace said, "lunch is served in conference room 2 today. Although, since you're new, I'll let you know that there is a practice among our group that we call 'fasting.' This is when we abstain from eating for a period of time."

"Why would anyone do that?" Archer asked.

"We do that periodically because it reminds us that material food is not what sustains us at our deepest level. His Highness said that He is the spiritual food that nourishes our soul, and fasting reminds us of this. Do you want to give it a try?"

Guuuuuurgle. "My stomach is saying no, but my heart is saying yes," Archer replied. "I definitely want to be in the right frame of mind for the mission, so I'll go with my heart on this one. Is not eating all I have to do to fast?"

"Typically people that fast spend time in the Prayer Room as well so they can realign their hearts and minds on His Highness and the Eternal Truths I showed you yesterday."

"I'm in," Archer said. "Are you still busy?"

"I'm still busy," Grace said. "But I'll come and get you when it's getting close to mission time. Is that okay?"

"That sounds perfect," Archer replied.

"Don't forget your sheet!" Grace said, handing Archer the laminated Eternal Truths.

Archer opened the door to the Prayer Room and sat on the couch. *I never thought I'd appreciate cricket sounds and bird chirps so much*, he thought. *But I guess being in a bunker several feet underground will do that to a guy.* Archer looked down at the sheet to refresh his memory.

Eternal Truths:

1) He loves you no matter what.
2) He desires eternal prosperity for you.
3) He died for you so that you may have citizenship in His kingdom.

Archer closed his eyes and became aware of his breathing. "He loves me no matter what," Archer said aloud. *Innnnnnn...ouuuuuuttttt.* "He desires eternal prosperity for me." *Innnnnnn...ouuuuuuttttt.* "He died for me so that I may have citizenship in His kingdom." *Innnnnnn...ouuuuuuttttt.* Archer's body entered a deeper state of relaxation with each inhale and exhale.

"Your Highness," Archer said, "thank you for dying for me and paying my fines so that I can know you and live with you in the kingdom. I couldn't have earned this privilege on my own. I deserved to be kicked out forever, but you acted on my behalf, and I'm forever grateful. You always deliver, no matter how bleak the circumstances appear. Right now, I'm really scared that I'll never see my family again, so please keep reminding me that you are always in control." Archer sat in silence and repeated in his head, *You're always in control*, over and over again.

"Fear not, Archer, for today, your mother shall walk free."

Startled, Archer opened his eyes and saw a man standing in front of him with a drawn sword in his hand. "His Highness has decreed it so."

"Who are you?" Archer asked.

"I am the commander of the army of the King." They both bowed. "I, and my troops, have been commanded to protect Nicole from the enemy and his soldiers. She is in good hands."

"Thank you," Archer replied as he fell to the floor in reverence. "Thank you, thank you, thank you."

"Get up, Archer," the man said as he picked Archer up and placed him back on the couch. "The time has come, and I must go to your mother. Close your eyes once more. Open them only after you feel the rush of wind come over you."

Archer did so. A mighty wind blew in the room as the man left Archer's presence. The air became still. Archer opened his eyes and stood up. "Thank you," he said aloud once more before he exited the Prayer Room.

"Perfect timing," Grace said. "I was just about to come and get you. How are you feeling?"

"Other than hungry," Archer said sarcastically, "better than ever. Today's gonna be a good day."

"You've got that right," Grace said. Grace led Archer to conference room 7.

"The Situation Room," he read aloud. "Seems legit." Archer opened the door.

"Welcome," Timothy said. "Make yourself at home. You can sit next to your buddy, Ty, if you want. We left a couple of seats open for you two."

"Woah," Archer exclaimed, looking around the room. "How many TVs are in here?"

"Enough to get the job done," Timothy replied. "We try to maintain real-time communication with our forces through the technology in this room."

"Sweet," Archer said.

Timothy proceeded to sit at the end of the table, facing the projector screen hanging down. "All right, team," Timothy said, "the time is officially 1730. Agent R has informed us that she and Nicole have begun their journey to the courtyard. The mission is progressing as planned. Archer, typically we would be able to receive periodic updates from rescue team members. However, we will not be able to receive visual or audio communications from our forces on the ground today. The Capital City camp heavily jams signals in the courtyard to prevent outside messaging from reaching the prisoners during recreation time. We are, however, able to track the rough location of our two rescue team members, Alpha and Omega. They are positioned just outside of the camp's boundary. If you turn your attention to the green radar screen with the concentric circles, you can observe two dots that indicate they are currently awaiting Nicole and Agent R, just outside the fence."

Archer watched as the two green dots blinked in place.

"Their job is to transfer the Metanoia to Nicole, if she so chooses. Does that make sense, Archer?"

"I'm tracking," Archer replied.

"Good," Timothy said. "We've also got radios and headsets over on that table that we will be using to speak with various members of the mission. It's a bit primitive, but they're the best communication tools we have that work in Capital City."

"Now, Agent R and your mother will spend the afternoon walking around the courtyard for some light exercise. The plan is for them to take their usual six laps around the courtyard. As you can see by the blueprints I've put up on the screen, the courtyard is surrounded by buildings on the eastern, southern, and western sides. The northern side is lined with a chain-link fence to give the prisoners a small view of nature, both for fresh air and to help them relax. As they pass by the northern side, we should be able to observe Alpha and Omega walking right beside them on the outer side of the fence. If she doesn't take the Metanoia, they are to report back to their starting position and wait for Nicole to return on the next lap and repeat the process as needed."

"Can't the guards see Alpha and Omega through the fence?" Archer asked.

"Good question," Timothy replied. "They have been outfitted with hi-tech camouflage that utilizes cameras on one side of the body and projects the image it sees onto the other side. This allows them to be virtually invisible."

"It's the same technology used in the escape car we drove in," Ty said.

"You all are so cool," Archer said. "I mean, what's next? Teleportation? Time travel?"

"We might be closer than you'd think," Timothy replied with a wink.

"I'm so glad I work here," Archer replied, shaking his head in disbelief.

"All right, Alpha and Omega are on the move," Timothy said.

Archer watched intently as the two dots moved horizontally across the screen. "How will we know if Mom takes the Metanoia?" Archer asked.

"Once the apparatus has been transferred to Nicole, Alpha and Omega will depart the scene and take a predetermined zigzagged path back to the escape vehicle. If she declines, they will take a straight-lined approach back to their rescue vehicle. Okay, look, they've returned to their original spot. We know Nicole has not taken it yet.

"Come on, Mom," Archer said. "You can do it."

The dots were mobile once again. "Come on," Timothy said. "Let's see some zigzags!" They blinked back to their starting location.

"No!" Archer shouted, pounding the table with his fist.

Grace and Ty patted Archer on the back.

"We've still got time, man," Ty said. "Stay strong."

Alpha and Omega blinked across the screen once more, only to have them return to their starting spot. Archer bowed his head and mumbled quietly to himself. "Your Highness, please provide a way out for my mom. I know she's scared, and I know she's hurting. This might be her only chance to escape. Please help her." Archer finished his prayer and locked his eyes on to the radar screen.

"There they go," Timothy said.

"I feel it," Ty said. "This is the one!"

The two dots returned to their original location.

Archer put his head in his hands. "I can't do it," he said. "She's not gonna take it."

"Two more laps," Timothy said. "Most Metanoia transfers occur at the tail end of our missions when it appears that all is lost. Keep your head up, Arch."

Ty and Grace interlocked their arms with Archer's, who was sitting in between them. The dots began travelling across the screen. They returned to their original location.

Archer began to cry. "Nooooooo!" he shouted toward the sky.

"Hey," Grace said, "it's going to be okay. Deep breaths. Slow your breathing. Come on. In and out. There you go. You're okay."

"I feel like I'm gonna pass out," Archer said, turning pale.

"Okay, someone lay him down horizontally so the blood can get back to his brain," Timothy instructed.

Grace and Ty picked Archer up from his seat and laid him down on the floor.

"Good," Timothy said. "Now elevate his feet a little bit. Perfect. Well done, you two."

Archer's breathing began to stabilize, and color returned to his face. His eyes shot open, and he sat up quickly. "The screen!"

"No," Ty said, holding him down, "you stay down there and rest for a little bit. We'll let you know what's going on."

Archer lay back down. "WELL?" he shouted. "What's going on?"

Timothy kneeled beside Archer. "Your mother didn't take it, Archer. I'm very sorry."

Archer broke down. "Why, Your Highness? Why didn't you do something? I asked for you to *do* something!" He sat up and put his head between his knees and continued to weep. "It's over," he said between sniffles and sobs. "She's gone!"

Timothy tried to console Archer. "There's a small chance we could try again sometime in the future, Archer. No one is ever too far gone. Sometimes even—"

"HOLD ON!" Grace shouted. "What are they doing?"

Archer and Timothy stood up.

"Alpha and Omega are back at their original spot," Timothy said. "They've been given strict orders to flee the scene after their sixth pass. I don't understand!"

Everyone in the room glued their eyes to the radar screen. The two dots remained motionless. "Did they get caught?" Ty asked.

"I don't know," Timothy replied. "Someone try reaching them on the emergency communication radio. Stat!"

Grace jumped at the opportunity. "I'm on it!" she said as she put on the headset attached to the radio labeled Emergency Comms. "Alpha, Omega. Do you copy?" Grace said. "I repeat. Alpha. Omega. Do you copy? Over." No response came over the radio. "Alpha. Omega. Do you copy?" Grace repeated. Silence.

"It was worth a shot. I knew their close-range jammers are too strong," Timothy said. "I'm going to have to call an emergency meeting. Ty, hand me that phone over on the—"

"THEY'RE ON THE MOVE! LOOK! THEY'RE RUNNING AWAY!" Archer shouted.

Everyone turned their attention to the radar screen. The two dots blinked away in the opposite direction of the reeducation camp.

"You're right!" Timothy exclaimed. "There they go! Ha! Ha! Get out of there safely, boys!"

Archer watched as they moved away from the camp on the radar. "Is that the zigzag or straight-line back route?" Archer asked, hoping it was the former.

"It's hard telling," Timothy responded. "Something weird must be going on. We'll just have to wait and find out what the situation is when they're able to communicate with us."

"So there's still a chance Mom took it?" Archer replied.

"There's still a chance!" Grace said, hugging Archer.

"Looks like it," Timothy said.

"Here's something you can do in the meantime," Timothy said. "Put on the headset for the radio that says, 'Nicole's Metanoia.' If, by some miracle, she responds, it will be channeled there."

"Roger that," he said as he donned the headset.

"We shouldn't expect her to respond immediately, though," Timothy said. "It takes roughly three minutes to reach the housing unit from the courtyard. The leaders that run the camp don't suspect anyone can be reached while inside, so she'll be able to send and receive audio messages from her cell."

Archer made sure the volume was turned all the way up. "Are we 100 percent sure it's on?" Archer said, pressing buttons.

"Yes!" Timothy said. "They're all on. Don't mess with anything. Just give it time."

One minute passed with no response. Two minutes. Three. "I'm not getting anything," Archer said.

"Any response from Alpha or Omega?" Timothy asked.

"Negative," Grace replied.

Timothy paced back and forth with his hands crossed behind his back. "Are we still tracking Alpha and Omega on the radar?" Timothy barked out.

"Yes," said a woman named Priscilla sitting near the front. "It looks like they're still on the move, and they have continued the same trajectory."

"Roger," Timothy said.

Several minutes elapsed. "Still nothing," Archer said.

"Same here," Grace echoed.

"Dang it!" Timothy shouted. He inhaled and exhaled audibly. "I didn't want to have to do this, but I think it's time to send in backup. Ty, can you hear me?"

"Yes, sir," he responded quickly.

"Make a call to the Capital City branch and inform them of the situation. Tell them Alpha and Omega aren't responding to our callouts, and we're afraid that they're in danger. Can you do that?"

"Yes, sir! Right away!" Ty said, dialing the numbers on the nearest phone.

"Grace, you keep trying your best to get ahold of them. I want a callout from you every ten seconds. Can you do that?"

"Yes, sir," she responded. "Alpha and Omega, do you respond?"

"Archer, can you come over here, please?" Timothy asked.

"Sure," Archer said.

Archer and Timothy sat down next to each other.

"What's up?" Archer asked.

"Archer," Timothy said, putting his hand on Archer's shoulder, "I want to be totally transparent with you because that's what you deserve. All signs point to something going very wrong today, and that probably spells trouble for your mother. Their treatment of prisoners caught trying to contact the outside is nothing short of despicable. You probably won't hear from your mother ever again, let alone see her. It was a risky mission to begin with, and I was the one who authorized it. I really thought we had considered every possible outcome, but I was wrong. I'm sorry, Archer. I just wanted you to hear it from me."

"It's not your fault," Archer responded. "Things don't always go the way we want them to go. That's life."

"You're unfortunately correct," Timothy said. "I think it would behoove you to take a moment to yourself to process all of this. Someone can take over for you at the radio."

"Thanks for shooting me straight," Archer said with a sigh. "I want to keep trying to reach her until the last possible moment, though."

"I appreciate your enthusiasm," Timothy said, "but we're long past the window where she would have responded."

"Well, I'm still not gonna give up," Archer said defiantly. "Is there something else I can do? There's gotta be something I can do."

Timothy thought for a moment. "There's really nothing you can do at this point," Timothy said. "Priority number one for you right now is to take care of yourself. Take a little breather. Maybe splash some water on your face and come back refreshed. I'll assess what our next steps will be and let you know once you're back."

"Yes, sir," Archer said, deflated. He walked over to the door to exit the Situation Room.

"Hey, Archer!" a man said, sitting at a radio.

Archer turned around.

"Come over here for a second," the man said.

Archer approached him. "Hi, I don't believe we've officially met. I'm Aquila, Priscilla's husband," he said, extending his hand.

"Archer," he said, shaking Aquila's hand.

"Pleasure to meet you, Archer. Look, I've been tasked with manning the 'Escape Car' station. I need to use the restroom and was wondering if you could take over for me briefly while I'm gone. Would that be okay?"

"Oh uhh, sure," Archer responded.

"Great," Aquila said. "I won't be but a minute." He took off his headset and stood up.

Archer replaced him in the seat and put on his headset.

"Under no circumstances are you to contact the driver of the escape car before they contact you. You could cause them to break their concentration. The only thing you need to do is sit there and wait for a callout. Do you understand?"

"Yes," Archer replied.

"Great," Aquila said. "I'll be right back." Aquila rushed toward the exit. "I knew I shouldn't have had that spicy chili right before this!"

The room was abuzz with noise as various radio operators tried to contact those on the ground.

"Anything yet?" Archer asked Grace, sitting next to him.

"Nada," she replied. "I'm really worried though. Look at the radar. Alpha and Omega are past the dot representing the escape car. Why would they do that?"

"I don't know," Archer replied. "Does Timothy know?"

"I'm not sure. I've been zoned in to my headset," Grace replied.

"You stay zoned in," Archer said. "I'll tell him."

"Good idea."

Archer swiveled around toward Timothy. "Hey, Timothy! Have you seen the ra—" Archer heard static in his headset.

"Archer! Didn't I order you to leave?" Timothy asked.

Archer grabbed the microphone and held it close to his mouth. "Hello! Hello! This is Archer! Do you hear me?" The static became louder. He could hear someone's muffled voice but couldn't make out the words. "Hello! This is Archer! Do you hear me? Please respond!" Static still overwhelmed the person's voice.

"Who is it?" Timothy asked.

"I can't tell what they're saying," Archer responded.

"Th…Nic…Arch—"

"I think I heard my name!" Archer shouted. "Yes! This is Archer!" he said into his headset. "Can you please repeat yourself?" Archer waited for a response.

"For the third time, I said, this is Nicole, and I want to talk to Archer."

"It's Mom!" Archer shouted. "I'm talking to Mom!"

"You sure are!" Nicole replied.

Team members in the room celebrated and high-fived.

"What…how…when—" Archer was at a loss for words.

"I don't even know where to begin, Archer," Nicole replied.

Timothy approached Archer. "Do you mind if I talk to Nicole for a quick second, Archer?" Timothy asked.

"Go right ahead," Archer replied, getting up from his seat. Archer hugged Grace and Ty, and they began jumping around in excitement.

"This. Is. Amazing!" Grace said. "His Highness always provides!"

"He sure does!" Ty exclaimed.

"All right, here you go, Archer," Timothy said, breaking up their celebration. "Sorry about that. I just had to take care of a couple logistic issues. Take as long as you need."

Archer put on the headset. "Mom, can you hear me?"

"Clear as a bell, honey."

"It's so good to hear your voice," Archer said.

"It's just as good to hear yours," she replied.

"How are you doing?" Archer asked. "How are you feeling? Do you have any injuries?"

"Nope," Nicole replied. "No injuries to speak of. I escaped the whole situation completely unscathed as far as I can tell. Overall, I'd say that I'm feeling overjoyed more than anything. I've got my freedom, I've got you and, most of all, I've got His Highness. I wouldn't be here talking to you if it weren't for Him."

"Praise be to the King!" Archer exclaimed.

Everyone in the room bowed.

"Amen!" Nicole replied.

"So, Mom," Archer said, "what made you decide to take the Metanoia?"

"Family," she replied succinctly.

Archer was confused. "Family?" Archer asked. "I thought you said in the other realm that our family was the reason your world was falling apart?"

"I did," she replied. "But I'm not talking about our earthly family. I'm talking about our forever family."

"Ahh," Archer said with a grin. "Tell me how you got to that point."

"Well," Nicole said, "my roommate, Rahab, asked me this evening, if I wanted to go on a walk with her during rec time. I said sure, and we agreed to take our daily six laps around the outdoor space. I had been sitting through class all day, so it was the perfect way to stretch my legs. So we left our cell and passed through the mandatory security checkpoints. Then we started our walk. It started out just like any normal walk we've had. You know, small chitchat, the weather. Things of that nature. Then, as we were approaching the turn by the fence facing the woods, Rahab whispers, 'I know about your visit with Archer in the Transcendent realm. We're taking *seven* laps today. More on lap two.' Oh I about fainted, Archer! But I kept it cool so the guards wouldn't be suspicious.

"We walk around to the same spot, and she says, 'Camouflaged soldiers are just outside the fence.' That was it. I looked out there, but I didn't see anybody. *This chick is crazy*! I thought to myself.

"Lap three: 'They have a hearing device for you to take to put in your ear.' Lap four: 'On the last lap, brush the fence with your outside hand open. You'll feel them place it in your hand.' Lap five: 'Act like you're scratching your head and place it in your ear as quickly as possible.' Lap six: 'Next lap, either take the device or shout to His Highness as loudly as possible at this exact spot, if you want to escape right here, right now.' 'No way! I can't draw that kind of attention to myself,' I whispered sharply. She didn't even slightly glance in my direction, though. As kooky as it sounded, I could tell she was dead serious.

"So we continued our walk, and I began to weigh my options. (1) I do nothing and play it safe. (2) I take the hearing device and risk getting caught with it, which could lead to being locked up forever were I to get caught with it. Or (3) I shout like a lunatic for some odd reason and risk nothing happening, which could also lead to being locked up forever."

"And all this has to be happening so fast, right?" Archer asked.

"It's actually the craziest thing," Nicole replied. "I've never experienced anything like it, but it was like time slowed down just for me, and everything around me was moving at normal speed. It was like I had all the time in the world to think about it."

"Wow," Archer replied. "That's pretty cool."

"It was indescribable." Nicole replied.

"So, anyway, we round our next two turns, and I find myself facing the chain-link fence: the only thing separating me from my freedom. *What do I do? What do I do?* I asked in my head repeatedly. On the one hand, I didn't want to do anything that would put me at risk for a punishment and risk never seeing my family again. Not to mention that I would be forfeiting my future for a cause that I wasn't even sure I believed in! But on the other hand, the visit I had with you seemed *so* real, and the fact that Rahab knew about it had to mean something, right? *What if Archer is right about the kingdom? What if I'm supposed to live there?* I thought.

"But then I heard, 'Get a grip, Nicole! It's all just coincidence. Do you really think everything you've ever been taught is part of some kind of grand conspiracy? There's no way everyone could be so collectively misled. That's impossible.' I mean, those are fair points, right?"

"Yeah, I suppose so," Archer replied. "You know those are lies, though, right?"

"Well," Nicole said, "now I know. It wasn't so obvious in the moment. My mind started to spiral into a bad place as we approached the fence. It felt like my heart was about to beat right out of my chest! I didn't know what the right thing to do was!"

Archer was gripped by the story.

"I eventually thought about you, and I thought about Jamie and Adrian and even your father. I just wanted to do what was right for the family. It was mental torture like I'd never experienced."

"I'm so sorry," Archer replied. "No son ever wants to hear their mom go through hardship like that. It's easier to listen to your story, though, because I know the ending. How did you get to the escape car? That wasn't part of the plan.

"Turn around, and I'll tell you."

Archer felt a tap on his shoulder. He turned around and saw his mother standing there, smiling from ear to ear. Archer shot up out of his seat and embraced his mother. Archer and Nicole cried tears of joy as thunderous applause filled the room. "I can't believe it. I thought I would never see you again," Archer said with his face buried in Nicole's shoulder.

"I feared the same, Archer. I really did," Nicole replied with her face resting on Archer's chest.

The two squeezed each other tightly. Finally, they released.

"This just doesn't feel like real life," Archer said. "I feel like I'm in a movie or something."

"You'd better believe it's real life," Nicole replied. "This is as real as real can get! Watch."

"Ow!" Archer shouted, as Nicole pinched his arm. "All right, I believe it!"

"We're so happy to have you here, Principal Coleman," Ty said as he hugged her.

"You know you're supposed to call me Nicole, you knuckle-head," she said chuckling. "And I'll be! If that isn't Grace Meyers," Nicole said.

"Welcome to the house-bunker, Nicole," Grace said as she hugged her.

Ty nudged Archer with his elbow in a suggestive manner. "Don't you have something you'd like to tell your mom, Archer? You know, something about a new female friend in your life."

Archer looked at Grace and Nicole and remembered. "Oh yeah! How could I forget? Mom," Archer said and then hesitated, "the ladies' room is down the hall right behind us. Grace can show you, but if you leave the room and take a left, the women's room should be the—"

"No, you silly boy!" Grace said as she took Archer's hand and kissed him.

"Oh right—" Archer said.

"YES! I knew it!" Nicole shouted. "I always had a feeling you two would end up with each other! Oh I'm so happy!" Nicole embraced Archer and Grace in one big hug.

"Aww, thanks Mrs. Coleman…sorry…I mean, Nicole!" Grace said.

"That's okay, sweetie. I'll let it slide…this time," Nicole said with narrowed eyes.

"Okay, Mom," Archer said, "I'm dying to hear how you got out. What say the four of us settle down in one of the conference rooms, and you can tell us all about it?"

"I'd love to," Nicole replied.

"Do you mind if we tag along?" Sasha said, standing beside Aaron.

"You two are here too?" Nicole asked.

"We sure are," Aaron said. "In fact, we've been here a very long time. We worked alongside your father for many years. He was a great man."

"Thank you," Nicole said. "I see now that he was truly a man of great character."

"Can I listen in too?" Timothy asked.

"What about us?" Priscilla asked.

"Wait, what did I miss?" Aquila asked as he was reentering the room.

"Yes, absolutely!" Nicole said. "How about we just make ourselves comfortable in this here fancy room, and I can clue you all in at the same time? Sound good?"

"Works for us!" Timothy replied for the group. "Peter, while we're doing that, keep trying to reach Alpha and Omega. Can you do that for me?"

"Yes, sir!" Peter said.

Everyone found a seat, with Nicole sitting at the head of the table.

"Before you start," Sasha asked as they sat down at the table, "would you like some coffee?"

"That would be delightful. Thank you," Nicole replied.

"Let's hear it, Mom!" Archer said. "I can't wait any longer!"

Nicole took a sip of her coffee and began. "What was the last thing I said? Oh right! I was running through my options as Rahab and I were about ten feet from the spot where the guards couldn't hear us. As we got a little closer, I decided I wasn't going to say or do anything. I was just going to finish our walk and go back to my room. No harm, no foul.

"And you know, I felt good about the decision. I'd even say I had come to peace with it. That is…until I heard His voice. He said: 'The enemy owns you as a slave, and slaves do not belong to the family of their master. Shake off your chains and come back to your forever family, Nicole. We are all waiting for you. Trust me.' We arrived not even a second later, and I let out, 'SET ME FREE, MY SAVIOR AND MY LORD!' as loud as I could possibly scream from somewhere inside of me that I didn't even know existed. I didn't think about the words. I didn't think about anything. It just exploded out of me, like a bullet out of a gun.

"Once I had said it, Rahab whispered, 'I'm proud of you. I'll see you again one day,' before she went running and screaming back to the guards to keep her cover from being blown. Nothing was happening initially, other than multiple guards sprinting in my direction to handcuff me. But, suddenly, three mighty oak trees from the other side of the fence came crashing down one after the other on the fence like a lumberjack had just felled them. *Boom!* One slammed onto the ground, taking down a section of the fence. *Boom*! Down came the next one. *Boom*! The third one came crashing down, taking down more of the fence. 'Run!' I heard Him say to me. So that's what I did. I hopped on top of the middle tree and ran as fast as I could on the trunk toward the outside world. I didn't look back, not even for a millisecond. The only thing I remember was one prison guard yelling, 'YOU'LL BE BACK! WE'LL FIND YOU!' 'FAT CHANCE!' I yelled right back at him."

"Nice!" Archer said, high-fiving Nicole.

She continued, "Sirens started blaring, and dogs started snarling. But I kept running until I was past the fence line, at which point I hopped off the tree and was immediately grabbed on both of my arms. 'GET OFF OF ME!' I screamed. 'Calm down, Nicole!' one of them said. 'We're here to rescue you. We're with Rahab.' I stopped fighting against them at that point. Too many weird things had happened for it all to be coincidental, so I surrendered and was just along for the ride. 'Here,' they said. 'Put this vest on and press the red button in the middle.' I put my head through it, strapped in, and pressed the button like they said. 'What does it do?' I asked. 'You're invisible now. We all are. Come on, let's get moving. We've got about a mile of woods to traverse.' 'All right, but I'm not very fast,' I said. 'Don't worry about that, ma'am. We've got you covered,' one of them said as they picked me up and put me over their shoulder in a fireman carry. My goodness, he was a mountain of a man. He ran like the wind even with me draped over his shoulders!

"I saw spotlights trying to locate us, and I heard the dogs getting closer. 'Are you sure we can outrun them?' I yelled. 'Positive, ma'am!' the other man said as he pulled the pin on a canister. 'This will release a smoke screen that should confuse their tracking ability!' he yelled back at me. 'Brilliant!' I shouted. He placed the canister down, and I watched the white smoke cover the area like a thick fog.

"We zigged and zagged through the woods, but the dogs managed to keep on our heels. The soldiers tried to evade them as best they could, but I could tell the dogs were well trained, and I could also tell that they looked very hungry. To make matters worse, I heard the engines of a group of motorbikes coming from behind us.

'Get back here with her!' I heard one of the authorities yell on one of them. 'NEVER!' yelled the man carrying me."

"Do you know how many people were chasing you?" Timothy asked.

"No, I haven't the foggiest," Nicole replied. "It all happened so fast. All I knew at that point was that I needed to hold on for dear life! And that's exactly what I did!"

Nicole continued, "Lucky for us, the terrain was quite bumpy with tree roots and natural ditches, so they couldn't hit top speed on their motorbikes. This bought a little bit of time before they caught up to us, but not much. 'They're gaining on us!' I yelled. 'Almost there!' the soldier carrying me yelled back. It wasn't but fifteen seconds later that I was heaved back over the man's shoulder and thrown in the open door of a running car. 'Welcome home, ma'am!' the man carrying me shouted. He proceeded to slam the door shut and smack the side of the car twice.

"'Are you in, Nicole?' the driver asked me. 'We've gotta go now!' 'Yes! I'm in!' I said, forgetting that I had my invisibility vest on. He yelled, 'Hold on to your hat!' as he stepped on the accelerator. Off we went, tires squealing and smoke rising in the air. I looked back and saw the dogs and the motorbikes zoom by in their continued pursuit of the soldiers." Nicole stopped and looked at Timothy. "Do we know how those two are doing?"

Timothy pointed to Peter.

"I have not heard from them as of yet," Peter replied.

"I sure do hope they're okay," Nicole said. "They saved my life."

"Alpha and Omega are our most highly-trained rescue members," Timothy replied. "If anyone can overcome the odds, it'll be them."

"I believe you," Nicole said. "I didn't think it was humanly possible for two people to be that fast and strong!"

"So, like I said," Nicole said. "I was safely in the getaway car. The driver said, 'Hello, Nicole. My name is Josh, and I'm here to transport you to our headquarters. How are you feeling?' I told him I was feeling fine and that I was ready to get as far away as possible from the reeducation camp. 'I can do that, ma'am,' he said."

Sasha interrupted. "Josh is one of our most experienced people at escorting people to where they're supposed to go. We made sure he was available for this mission."

"Well, I appreciate that," Nicole said. "He was a nice man and an even better driver! His handling of the car at that speed was very impressive.

"So, after a little bit of driving, he said, 'If you're comfortable with it, there is a phone in the middle console that you can turn on and communicate with your son.' 'Well, heck yeah!' I said. Of course I was comfortable with that! So I turned it on and tried to reach you, but all I heard was static. I kept trying and, eventually, I heard your voice. That was the moment I knew everything was going to be okay."

Archer smiled.

"Then we made the drive out here to Dad's old house, and the rest is history."

"Amazing," Aaron said. "Praise be to His Highness for engineering such a wonderful rescue mission!"

"Praise be!" many in the room shouted.

"Thank you so much for sharing, Nicole," Timothy said. "If there's nothing else you'd like to add, you and Archer are free to go decompress in one of our conference rooms. We will continue to monitor the whereabouts of our agents in the field, but you two are free to go."

"Thank you," Nicole said. "Thank you for everything you guys did for me. I feel like I don't deserve the love you all have shown me today."

"You more than deserve it," Timothy replied. "You have infinite inherent value, just like everyone else on the planet. And as Truth Tellers, we would rather die attempting to rescue a person than sit idly by while they remain enslaved to the enemy."

Nicole hugged Timothy, and Archer led the two out of the Situation Room.

Immediately Nicole grabbed Archer's arm. "Take me to the other realm."

"Right now?" Archer asked. "Are you sure you don't want to get cleaned up or grab a bite to eat?"

"No, Archer. I'm ready to meet Him for myself right now."

"All right! Your wish is my command," Archer said.

Together, they walked over to the Prayer Room and entered.

"Oh my gosh," Nicole said, "it is so soothing in here. Look at all these flowers and the little waterfall! This is just the kind of environment I need to calm down my nerves."

Archer instructed Nicole to lie down on the couch and close her eyes. "Take deep breaths and try to relax. In and out slowly. Good," Archer said.

"What should I be thinking about?" Nicole asked.

"You could think about a lot of different things," he replied. "Some people like to focus on the present moment. 'For the Present is the point at which time touches eternity.' One of the most famous Tellers wrote that long ago."

"That's beautiful," Nicole said.

"You could also set your mind on anything you know to be true or noble or right or pure or lovely or admirable or excellent or praiseworthy!"

"Wow, that's a smorgasbord of options to choose from!"

"Any of them will do," Archer said. "The cool thing is that the King is the source of any good thing you could possibly think of." Archer bowed. "If you want to cut right to the chase, you could think just about Him and have a conversation with Him directly."

"Me?" Nicole said. "There's no way He has time to talk to me."

"You don't know until you try," Archer replied.

Nicole took a deep breath. She began to form a picture in her mind of an old king with a long, white beard, sitting on his magnificent throne. "Hello?" Nicole said as she approached the throne. The king was unresponsive. She was the only one in his presence. "Hi, your highness. My name is Nicole Coleman. Can you hear me?" The old king continued to sit there quietly. "Am I in the right place?" she asked herself, looking around the room.

Suddenly, the King stood up and shouted, "Who dares be in my presence?"

236

Nicole crouched down in fear.

"Speak up, whoever you are!"

"Muh…muh…my name is Ni…Nicole Coleman, sir."

"Nicole, yes." he said. "I remember you. Come closer, my child."

Hesitant, Nicole slowly proceeded toward the throne.

"Don't be scared," he said. "We've met many times before. Don't you remember me?" The king grabbed under his chin and pulled off his mask, revealing the Prophet's face underneath.

Nicole shrieked and turned to run away.

"There's no one to come help you this time!" the Prophet shouted. The Prophet lunged at Nicole and grabbed her. Icicles began to form where his thin, pale fingers encircled her upper arm. She watched momentarily as the freezing effect spread down her arm and up to her neck. Without thinking, Nicole let out a bloodcurdling shriek and bit into the flesh of his forearm.

"GAHHH!" the Prophet shouted as he released his grip.

Nicole took off away from the throne.

"GET BACK HERE!" he shouted.

Water flowed down Nicole's arm as the encapsulating ice melted away. Terrified, Nicole banged on the walls with her fists. "LET ME OUT OF HERE!" she screamed.

"NO ONE CAN HEAR YOU, YOU FOOL!" the Prophet shouted, laughing maniacally.

Nicole rammed her shoulder in the wall repeatedly. The wall held its shape. "Please, I just want out of this nightmare." She whimpered as she slid down onto the floor near the far corner of the room, weeping into her hands.

"HA! GIVE UP, HAVE YOU? I ALWAYS KNEW YOU WERE WEAK!" the Prophet bellowed.

Nicole felt utterly and completely hopeless.

Suddenly, she heard a voice of hope. "Face him directly. It's time to stop running away from him."

"I can't!" she defied. "I won't!"

"He will not harm you any longer, if you stand up to him and face him," the voice said without hesitation.

"It's impossible," Nicole replied. "He's so large and powerful."

"Trust Me."

Nicole sat for a few seconds, still sniffling and crying. Shaking in fear, Nicole reluctantly stood up and slowly turned around. She battled internally to take her first, small step toward the Prophet, all while shielding her eyes.

"Make eye contact."

Nicole removed her hands from over her eyes. She cautiously opened them and looked the Prophet in the eyes. His beady, yellow eyes beamed back at her.

"Ahh, I see you've come to your senses," he said, extending his arms invitingly.

Nicole gained confidence with each step she took toward him. The Prophet shrank in size the closer she moved toward him.

"Wait! What's happening to me?" he shouted.

Nicole increased her pace. The faster she ran, the smaller he got.

"HALT! DON'T COME ANY FURTHER!" he ordered in a puny, high-pitched voice.

Nicole continued her charge toward him. She didn't stop until she reached the Prophet standing in front of the throne. The Prophet stood three inches tall. Nicole raised her foot to stomp on him. "Leave him!" she heard. Nicole stopped the momentum of her leg downward. "I will take care of him properly when the time has come. Now look up and behold." Nicole observed an open door behind the throne. "Run to me."

Nicole stepped over the cowering Prophet and burst through the doorway, into the open arms of the King.

CHAPTER 13

Commencement

"Welcome home, Nicole. It is so good to have you here," the King said as he wiped away a tear from her face. "I've been longing for this moment."

"I have too," Nicole replied through sobs and sniffles. "I just wish I had come sooner."

"You arrived at the perfect time, Nicole," the King said. "I couldn't be more pleased with you."

Nicole looked around in awe of the beauty.

"What do you see, my daughter?" the King asked.

"I see...perfection," she ultimately recognized. "I mean, just look at the crystal-clear river and the trees that are growing next to them. It's easily the most beautiful natural site I've ever seen!"

"Good observation," the King noted. "That is the river of the water of life, and those are the trees of life. Everyone who drinks of that water and eats of those fruits will never again thirst or hunger. And you, my beloved child, have done this. You are now experiencing life to the fullest."

"No more hunger or thirst?" Nicole asked. "Is there food in the kingdom?"

"Indeed there is," the King replied. "Food has a different purpose here. Decaying earthly bodies utilize food as a way to slow down that decay. Here, there is no cellular decay. Food and drink are purely for enjoyment in the kingdom."

"This place *is* heaven!" Nicole exclaimed.

The King laughed. "Because decay does not exist here," He added, "there is no more death or mourning in my kingdom. The old, earthly order of things has completely passed away here."

"This is all just incredible," Nicole said. "Thank you, Your Highness."

"It's my pleasure," the King said. "I would have gladly created all this, even if you were the only person to share it with."

"Thankfully, I'm not!" Nicole replied.

"Amen to that!" the King said. "There are a great multitude here that no one can count, from every nation, tribe, people, and language. It is truly a wonderful sight to behold people of such diversity communing together in love forever."

"I would very much like to see people getting along in this manner," Nicole asked. "I'm so tired of the constant fighting between people on earth. Is there a place you could take me to experience that kind of communal love in action?"

"Of course," the King said. "Right this way."

"Woah," Nicole said, stepping onto the golden path. "It's as pure as transparent glass! And look at all the stones in the city walls. They're so pretty!"

The King led Nicole to the neighborhood where citizens of the kingdom reside. Nicole felt the loving Spirit that connected everyone in the neighborhood as she watched them interacting with one another.

"Nicole! Over here!" Nicole looked and saw her parents standing on the front lawn of their home.

"Go," the King instructed. "I will catch up with you later."

Nicole hugged the King once more and ran toward Franklin and Ruth. "Mom! Dad!" she said, hugging them tightly. "It's been so long! How are you two doing?"

"Better than ever, now that you're here!" Franklin replied.

Nicole let go of her hug and stepped back to view them. "You two look amazing!" Nicole said.

"Oh honey," Ruth replied, cheerfully, "you look just as beautiful as I remember!"

"You really do," Franklin added.

The three walked on to the front porch and sat down. "Oh my goodness," Nicole said, smiling. "My heart is so full right now."

"You'd better get used to that feeling while you're here," Franklin said. "It never goes away."

"I will gladly get used to this feeling," she replied, joyfully.

"Would you like a glass?" Ruth asked, holding a pitcher full of bright yellow lemonade. "Sure!" Nicole answered.

Ruth filled a glass and handed it to her daughter.

"Mmm!" Nicole exclaimed, after taking a sip. "That is the best tasting lemonade I've ever had."

"Thank you, dear!" Ruth replied. "I just followed the recipe!"

Nicole watched the happenings of the neighborhood for a moment and then turned to her parents. "I'm so excited to hear all about the adventures you had during your earthly lives," Nicole said. "We have so much to catch up on!"

"We're excited to hear about yours as well!" Ruth replied. "How about you start and then we'll go?"

"I'd love to," Nicole said. She took another drink of lemonade and put it down on the table. "Before we start sharing stories, though," Nicole said, "I just wanted to say something."

"Anything," Franklin replied.

"I want to say I'm sorry for the way I treated you two at times on earth, especially you, Dad. I was young and immature and, frankly, I just missed my dad. I couldn't comprehend any good reason why a father would desert his family. But I see now that you did what was best for us. Thank you. And thank you, Mom, for taking care of the family by yourself. It couldn't have been easy."

"It was no picnic. That's for sure," Ruth said, chuckling. "But your father and I vowed, from the beginning of our marriage, that we would always do what was best eternally for our children. It just turned out that what we had to do was very difficult. Being here with you and others more than makes up for the momentary difficulties we experienced during our earthly lives. Thankfully those times are over, and now it's time to celebrate together!"

"Your mother's exactly right," Franklin added. "I completely forgive any hard feelings you had toward me at the time. It was a difficult age for you to have a parent leave the house. In fact, I feel like I'm the one that should apologize, leaving all you kids."

"No, Dad," Nicole said, "you did the right thing, protecting us like that. I'm forever grateful for the sacrifices you two made for us."

"That means a lot, dear," Ruth replied.

"Mom, you just mentioned you were ready to celebrate with me and 'others,'" Nicole said. "Are there any other family or friends that live in the kingdom that I would know?"

"There sure are, and they're all very excited to see you," Franklin replied. "Come on out, gang!"

Archer walked through the front door to the porch, carrying a cake with one candle burning. "Surprise!" he and a group of around thirty people shouted.

Nicole covered her mouth in shock. "Grandpa Jasper! Aunt Alice!" she shouted. "Oh my goodness, there's so many of you that I haven't seen in so long!"

"Happy birthday, Nicole!" the group shouted in unison.

"Birthday?" Nicole said, confused. "I don't think it's my birthday."

"It sure is!" Ruth said. "Today you've been born again! This time you've been born into the kingdom. And let me tell you, I'm enjoying this one a whole lot more than your first one!"

"Me too!" Nicole replied.

"Blow out the candle so we can dig in!" Archer exclaimed. Nicole blew out the candle, and the party went inside to cut the cake.

"Wow," Nicole said, "I really love what you've done with the place! The wood interior is so extravagant. And the furniture looks so comfortable!"

"Thank you," Franklin said, "But we can't take any credit for it. We were blessed with this home upon our arrival into the neighborhood. In fact, there will be one awaiting you, too, when you pass on from the Earthly realm to live here permanently."

"Sweet!" Nicole replied.

"Does everyone have a slice of cake?" Ruth shouted over the other conversations. "Okay, good. Let's move this celebration to the backyard where we have more space for everyone!"

The group slowly migrated to the backyard. "Mom!" Archer said, sitting down on the patio, "have you met Great-Uncle Rick before? The stories from his time as a Truth Teller are crazy!"

"Of course I remember Uncle Ricky," Nicole said as she hugged him. "It's been years...shoot, decades at this point, since I last saw him, but I could never forget him! How's life up here, Ricky?"

"Just perfect," Ricky said, flashing a big, toothy smile. "I've never felt better. All the heartache and pains of earthly life melted away the moment I arrived. Being in the constant presence of His Highness is an ineffable joy."

"It truly is amazing," Nicole replied.

"Do you know what's even more amazing?" Ricky asked.

"What's that?"

"His Highness is not finished yet."

"Elaborate," Nicole said.

"The Earthly realm and the Transcendent realm were originally designed to coexist," Ricky explained. "They began that way, in fact. There was no divide between the two. We humans decided that we wanted to live apart from Him, so He separated the two. Fortunately for us, He always had a rescue plan that He would enact at an appointed time in the future where He will usher into existence a new kingdom and a new earth that will overlay on top of each other. They will exist together in harmony, just as His Highness planned from the beginning."

"So this current kingdom isn't our final destination?" Archer asked.

"Nope," Ricky replied. "There is an appointed Day that His Highness will judge the people of earth, both the living and the dead. Fortunately everyone here has accepted his free gift of grace to pay for our misbehaviors so that we may be tried and ruled not guilty in His sight. From that Day forward, we will live with Him in the new kingdom and the new earth forever and ever."

"And that Day can't come soon enough!" Archer shouted.

"Amen!" everyone around the table shouted.

The group continued to chat, and Nicole was almost finished with her cake when she heard singing out in the distance.

"Your celebration!" Archer shouted. "It's starting soon!"

"I thought this was my celebration?" Nicole asked.

"No, your official celebration down at the town center!" Archer replied. "Come on!" Archer grabbed Nicole by the hand, and they beelined to the town center.

Nicole admired the balloons and streamers decorated everywhere as they approached the party. The live concert also caught her attention. "They sure know how to throw a party here!" she exclaimed.

"Oh yeah," Archer affirmed. "They pull out all the stops for these celebrations, and for good reason! There's nothing to celebrate more than someone coming back to live in the kingdom!"

The two walked another block on the golden path. "This is where I have to leave you," Archer said, urging his mother forward. "Keep following the golden path, and you'll be right where you're supposed to be! We'll all be in the crowd, watching! Enjoy!"

"Oh…okay!" Nicole said. "I love you!"

"I love you, too, Mom! Have fun!"

Nicole continued forward until the golden path transitioned into a red carpet. She followed it to the stage, where she found her seat and sat down.

The King began the processions of the celebration. "Welcome, everyone!"

The crowd quieted down. "As you all know, we are here to celebrate the group of people seated behind me who have decided to come home."

The crowd erupted in cheers at these words.

Archer smiled, seeing his mother so filled with joy. He began to think about the journey both of them had taken to reach the kingdom.

Franklin nudged Archer with his elbow. "That was you not too long ago!" he said. "Can you believe how many people show up on stage each celebration?"

"It's a brilliant sight to behold," Archer replied.

"Truly," Franklin said.

Archer tuned back in to the message.

"They have joined my team and donned my golden yoke," the King said as the crowd rose to their feet and applauded.

Nicole smiled as she observed the golden yoke appear around her shoulders.

"Welcome home, my beloved children," the King said to conclude His speech.

The crowd maintained their standing ovation. Many people whistled, hooted, and hollered for their loved ones on stage.

"Look how happy she is!" Archer shouted.

"Way to go, Nicole!"

Nicole exited the stage and hugged all her family and friends in attendance. Soon after, the party returned to Franklin and Nicole's house where the group danced and played games until, one by one, the guests returned to their homes.

"Bye, Abe!" Nicole said as the last guest left the party. "Love the top hat, by the way! Phew!" she said, plopping down on the couch. "It sure feels good to sit down. I feel like it's been nonstop celebration from the moment I got here!" Nicole kicked off her shoes and lay down. "Oh, wow," she exclaimed. "This couch is divine. I feel like I could doze off right here, right now."

"Yeah, me too," Archer replied with heavy eyelids.

"This means it's time for you two to depart our presence once again," Franklin said.

"Aww man, I don't want to leave yet," Nicole replied.

"See it as an opportunity," Franklin said. "You two have important work to do while you're still living earthly lives."

"You're right," Nicole said, struggling to keep her eyes open.

"Before you go, I'd like to impart some wisdom on both of you that I read recently," Franklin said, pulling out a piece of paper. "It goes like this: 'Make every effort to add to your faith, goodness, and to goodness, knowledge, and to knowledge, self-control, and to self-control, perseverance, and to perseverance, godliness, and godliness, mutual affection, and to mutual affection, love. For if you possess these qualities in increasing measure, they will keep you from being ineffective and unproductive in your knowledge of the King.'"

Ruth and Franklin bowed.

Archer and Nicole had already fallen asleep and dissipated into thin air.

"I told you that you should have gone with the shorter version," Ruth said, chuckling.

Archer and Nicole opened their eyes simultaneously. They had returned to the Prayer Room. Archer stood up and stretched, twisting his torso side to side. "Boy, Transcendental realm travel really does a number on my back! How about you, Mom?"

Nicole did not respond. After a few seconds, she began to shake her head. "Thank you, Archer," she said.

"For what?" he asked.

"For being such a brave young man and standing up for the Truth, even when it was difficult. I wouldn't be here right now if it weren't for you."

"No, Mom," Archer replied. "All of your thanks should be directed to the King."

They both bowed.

"I'm just a little pencil in His hands. He does the thinking and He does the writing. Always thank Him."

Nicole smiled and closed her eyes. "Thank you, Your Highness, for your everlasting love."

"Amen," Archer said.

Archer opened the door for Nicole, and they proceeded to exit the Prayer Room. He closed the door, and they stood together, watching the organized chaos play out in front of them. Many workers sat at their desks, typing away, while others rushed purposefully across the room. The scene resembled bees buzzing around their hive.

"Another nation has adopted the HQ system!" one woman shouted to a coworker. "I'm gonna need more workers sent there. Get on it, ASAP!"

"Are you serious? That's the third one this week!" a man yelled back. "I'll get right on it!"

Archer looked at his mother, then back ahead. "Let's get to work."

ABOUT THE AUTHOR

Born in Indiana, Kyle Richardville was raised in a Christian household by a loving, farming family. He grew up fascinated by the natural world and is now an agricultural researcher. The interconnectedness of God's creation is a wonder to behold to him and only strengthens his beliefs that God is real, God is loving, and God's words are true. Kyle is a husband, an uncle, a brother, a son and, most importantly, a follower of Jesus Christ. He currently lives with his wife, Michelle, in North Carolina.

The main catalyst for this book was his eight wonderful nieces and nephews that are quickly approaching their high school and college years, where they will no doubt encounter difficult questions pertaining to their Christian beliefs. Leaning into these difficult questions rather than shying away from them only served to strengthen Kyle's faith throughout college and early adulthood, so he hopes that *Beast of Burden* provides a fun and thought-provoking way for young and old alike to challenge their beliefs and come out the other side with a stronger, more durable faith.